THE STATE OF THE ENVIRONMENT ATLAS

Joni Seager is a Canadian who teaches geography and women's studies at the University of Vermont. She has worked on environmental issues for several years, especially on militarism and the environment. Her previous books include *Women in the World: An International Atlas* and *Earth Follies: Coming to Feminist Terms with the Global Environmental Crisis.*

THE STATE OF THE ENVIRONMENT ATLAS

Joni Seager

with Clark Reed and Peter Stott

PENGUIN BOOKS

PENGUIN BOOKS

Published by the Penguin Group
Penguin Books Ltd, 27 Wrights Lane, London W8 5TZ, England
Penguin Books USA Inc., 375 Hudson Street, New York, New York 10014, USA
Penguin Books Australia Ltd, Ringwood, Victoria, Australia
Penguin Books Canada Ltd, 10 Alcorn Avenue, Toronto, Ontario, Canada M4V 3B2
Penguin Books (NZ) Ltd, 182–190 Wairau Road, Auckland 10, New Zealand

Penguin Books Ltd, Registered Offices: Harmondsworth, Middlesex, England

First published 1995
10 9 8 7 6 5 4 3 2 1

Edited and co-ordinated for Myriad Editions by Anne Benewick
with Chris Schüler and Candida Lacey

Design by Corinne Pearlman

Maps created by Angela Sitch and Jennifer Mexter for
Line + Line Limited, Thames Ditton, Surrey

Printed and bound in Hong Kong
Produced by Mandarin Offset Limited

Printed on paper made from pulp from managed Canadian forest,
reforested by a mixture of planting and natural regeneration

CONTENTS

INTRODUCTION

In the late 1980s, I wrote in the introduction to the first edition of this book that "concern is the catalyst that shapes this atlas. We share with many the belief that habitat earth, in the late 20th century, is in growing trouble." In the mid-1990s, there is even greater reason for concern. Scientists still debate whether climate change is occuring, but the weight of scientific opinion appears to be swinging slowly towards a confirmation that human activities have already altered the chemistry and dynamics of the atmosphere, and that greater changes most likely lie ahead. The assault on land, air and water by industrial and agricultural chemicals is unrelenting; of the almost two dozen pesticides that Rachel Carson identified in the early 1960s as especially deadly, two-thirds are still in use around the world. Scores of new chemicals are introduced each year, and most are untested for their environmental efficacy. Militaries continue to exert extraordinary pressures on the earth's ecosystems and, despite the end of the Cold War, there appears to be little relief from ever-proliferating militarism. The nature of economic activity and consumption in the rich, industrialized world continues to take a disproportionate toll on the global commons. Species are being made extinct at an accelerating rate, and our scientific capacity to monitor the existence — let alone the well-being — of most species cannot keep pace with the destruction. Toxic wastes, including nuclear materials, continue to accumulate at an alarming rate. As modern industrialization spreads around the world, so "modern" pollution and illnesses follow in its wake.

Many problems identified in the 1980s have become more acute (as has our understanding of them,) while new problems have come into view. The Rio Earth Summit, an international conference sponsored by the United Nations in 1992, brought governments together in a highly visible, public forum to forge an agenda for global environmental action. Vested commercial interests and the imperatives of nationalism subverted many of the good intentions brought to the Rio meetings, but there were several positive results from this summit, such as the treaties (albeit weakened) which were signed on biodiversity and global climate change. As importantly, the Rio meetings gave broad exposure to more radical analyses, developed by non-governmental organizations (NGOs), women's groups, and environmental groups during the 1980s, of the links between poverty, development and the environment, and of the environmental costs of economic inequities. As we move into the 21st century, it is becoming increasingly evident that social, environmental, and economic issues are intertwined, and that the state of the environment is linked to the state of human health. But while concern is rapidly growing about health in general, doctors and scientists remain surprisingly reluctant to explore the specific links between health problems and environmental conditions; where links have been made, it is largely due to pressure from grassroots environmental and health groups.

Not all the news is grim. There are some positive signs of real environmental progress. West European states have made considerable progress in reducing sulphur dioxide emissions, the principal component of acid rain. An international agreement to eliminate the production and use of chlorofluorocarbons (CFCs), the principal cause of ozone depletion, has won widespread international approval and compliance. Through funding commitments made to the Global Environmental Facility (GEF), rich states are beginning to acknowledge their responsibility for providing assistance to poor states for global environmental protection. In most countries, there is growing public support for environmental protection – although this is not easy to measure. Public awareness has been enhanced, in part, by the many businesses and industries which are discovering that "going green" can be profitable. Throughout the 1990s, there has been a growth of green businesses and rapid expansion of the environmental clean-up industry.

This second edition of the atlas is entirely revised and updated. On several maps, we highlight the connections between poverty, development, and environment. New maps on meat consumption, cars, tourism, and sports hunting underscore the environmental costs of wealthy, Western lifestyles. We also present new information on ecological destruction in the former USSR, on green attitudes, on health, and on the protection of wilderness. Despite the growth in interest, surprisingly few new data sources on the global environment have been made available to the public domain over the past few years. Computer networks have facilitated the transfer of some environmental data, but much information about the environment remains proprietary or confined to the privileged domain of specialists. The rapid political changes since the late 1980s have, if anything, made international data even more difficult to collect. For example, there is little data for the new states of the former USSR, for the fragmented states of the former Yugoslavia, or for new states such as the Czech Republic and Slovakia. Most of these states are facing severe financial and political challenges, and may take several years even to establish the infrastructure needed to collect data.

The main commitment in this atlas remains to a global view. Global mapping highlights patterns and relations among states, and invites comparative analysis. But, as in the earlier edition, we are well aware that a global perspective has limitations and frustrating shortcomings. It is virtually impossible, for example, to detail small-scale environmental issues and actions. The proliferation of grassroots environmental activism is one of the most positive features of the late 1980s and early 1990s, but we cannot really show its presence. Small-scale, community-based environmental activism has influenced governments and institutions throughout the world — exposing the impacts of militarism in the former USSR and the United States; creating a greenbelt movement in Kenya; revitalizing a tradition of forest protection in India; bringing international visibility to the nuclear plight of Pacific islanders. Grassroots groups all over the world, most of which are initiated and powered by women, have also brought to light a host of local issues many of which have been overlooked by larger environmental groups.

The role of individuals in environmental relations is mediated by gender, class, ethnicity and religion. Men and women, for example, have different relationships to the large institutions — governments, militaries, industrial corporations — that hold the balance of power in environmental issues. Similarly, the implications of environmental decay, and the experience of environmental disruption, are often different for men and women, for rich and poor, for elites and the disenfranchised. These patterns are virtually impossible to illustrate in a global survey but, wherever possible, I have tried to discuss social, political and gender issues in the Notes to the maps on pages 101–27.

I remain convinced that an informed citizenry is the environment's best hope, and I would like to think that this atlas brings that hope a little closer.

ACKNOWLEDGMENTS

There are several key individuals to whom I owe particular thanks. Clark Reed and Peter Stott provided stellar research assistance; they conducted the primary research for several of the maps, and their contributions have helped to shape the whole. My thanks to Sheldon Krimsky and Ann Urosovich at Tufts University for coordinating the arrangements which made it possible for Clark and Peter to work on the atlas. The Dean's Office and the Department of Geography at the University of Vermont provided partial financial support for the travel necessary for coordinating the editing and production of this atlas. My thanks especially to Andrew Bodman in the Geography department for his encouragement and support.

Anne Benewick is the indefatigable force behind the atlas series; without her extraordinary effort on editing and production, this atlas would still be little more than doodles on scraps of paper. Candida Lacey and Chris Schüler provided invaluable editorial assistance throughout the project, and the maps were creatively realized by Line + Line. The outstanding design and illustration for this atlas is the work of Corinne Pearlman, who also helped us to think through the editorial content of several of the maps.

And last but far from least my thanks to Cynthia Enloe who provided constant encouragement, keen insights, and a seemingly-endless supply of bits of data.

I would like to thank the following individuals and organizations for help with particular maps: Miriam Allman, Wessell Library, Tufts University; Don Aurand, Maritime Spill Response Corporation; Gilbert Bamkobeza, Ozone Secretariat, Nairobi; Robbins Barstow, Cetacean Society International; Basel Convention Secretariat, Geneva; Pauleen Boucher, Wessell Library, Tufts University; Dirk Bryant, World Resources Institute; John Caddy, FAO; Marva Coates, FAO, Washington DC; CITES Secretariat, Geneva; Linda Durfee, Wessell Library, Tufts University; Jim Elkins, NOAA; Ecotourism Society, Vermont; George Furness, Conservation Treaty Support Fund, Maryland; Gaffney, Cline & Associates; Andrea Gaskey, TRAFFIC, Washington DC; Peter Haber, Switzerland; Margaret Gooch, Wessell Library, Tufts University; Kevin Gurney, Institute for Energy and Environmental Research, Maryland; Dexter Hinkley, Climate Change Office, Environmental Protection Agency; Chuck Johnson, Nuclear Free America; Nicholas Lenssen, Worldwatch Institute; Judith Mackay; Jean McManus, Wessell Library, Tufts University; Bill Moomaw, Fletcher School of Law and Diplomacy, Tufts University; Nick Morgan, Greenpeace USA; Ann Muller, Committee to Abolish Sport Hunting; Connie Murtagh, Greenpeace USA; Lars Nordberg, UN Economic Commission for Europe; Marice Pelletier, Friends of the Earth Canada; Connie Reik, Wessell Library, Tufts University; Michael Renner, Worldwatch Institute; Denise Rouleau, New England Electric Company; D.J. Schubert, Fund for Animals, Washington DC; Miriam Seltzer, Ginn Library, Tufts University; Leonard Sklar, International Rivers Network; Jim W. Thorsell, IUCN; Mike Weber.

Joni Seager
Somerville, Massachusetts, July 1994

Part One

WORLDS APART

1	Haiti
2	Cambodia, Uganda, Mali
3	Albania, Burkina Faso
4	Bangladesh, Malawi, Namibia
5	Sri Lanka, Sudan
6	Fiji, Senegal
7	Jamaica, Vietnam
8	Indonesia, Kenya
9	India, Pakistan
10	Afghanistan, Paraguay
12	Bolivia, Costa Rica, Zimbabwe
13	Laos, Syria
17	China
18	Algeria, Morocco
19	S. Korea, Mongolia, Zambia
26	Ireland, Tunisia
27	Mexico, South Africa
33	Hungary
35	Netherlands
43	Israel, U.A.E.
61	Denmark
63	Romania, Venezuela
68	Norway
71	Brazil, U.K.
78	Iceland, Switzerland
81	France
99	Italy
107	Japan
116	New Zealand, Portugal
120	Sweden
125	Canada
159	U.S.A.

DOMESTIC WATER USE
early 1990s
gallons per person per day

1 gallon = 4.5 litres

Source: *World Resources 1992-93*

GREENLAND
(Den)

ICELAND

CANADA

NORWAY
SWEDEN

DENMARK
IRELAND UNITED KINGDOM
NETH. POLAND
PERU GERMANY
CZECH
FRANCE AUS. HU
B-H3Y
ITALY

PORTUGAL SPAIN AL
GR

UNITED STATES
OF AMERICA

ATLANTIC
OCEAN

MOROCCO
31%

TUNISIA
17%

ALGERIA LIBY

MEXICO
71%

74%

BAHAMAS
44%

CUBA
JAMAICA
BELIZE HONDURAS
HAITI
DOMINICAN
REPUBLIC
PUERTO RICO (US)

WESTERN SAHARA

MAURITANIA

CAPE VERDE
ISLANDS

46%
MALI NIGER

54°
CHA

GUATEMALA
EL SALVADOR
NICARAGUA
27%

DOMINICA
BARBADOS
GRENADA
TRINIDAD & TOBAGO

SENEGAL
GAMBIA
GUINEA-BISSAU

BURKINA
FASO
BENIN

COSTA RICA
PANAMA
46%

VENEZUELA
GUYANA
SURINAME
FRENCH GUIANA (Fr)

GUINEA
SIERRA LEONE
LIBERIA

CÔTE d'
IVOIRE
GHANA
NIGERIA
C A

20%

26%

COLOMBIA

TOGO
EQUATORIAL GUINEA
SAO TOME & PRINCIPE
CAMEROON
37%

PACIFIC
OCEAN

ECUADOR
56%

GABON
CONGO
Z

42%

PERU

64%

BRAZIL

ANGOLA

BOLIVIA

NAMIBIA

CHILE

39%
PARAGUAY

50%

SO
AFF

URUGUAY

ARGENTINA

FALKLAND ISLANDS
(UK)

LEVELS OF HUMAN DEVELOPMENT *1990*
Based on the UN Human Development
Index, a combined index measuring
income, literacy rates, average years of
schooling, and life expectancy.

- high
- medium
- low
- no data
- decrease in human development
  index ranking *1970-90*

**PROPORTION OF POPULATION LIVING IN
ABSOLUTE POVERTY** *1977-89* percentages

- 70% or more
- 40-69%
- below 40%

Source: UNDP, *Human Development Report 1993.*

TO HAVE — AND HAVE NOT 1

The Earth Summit at Rio de Janeiro in 1992 made clear that poverty — including inequities between the rich world and the poor world — is at the root of many environmental threats.

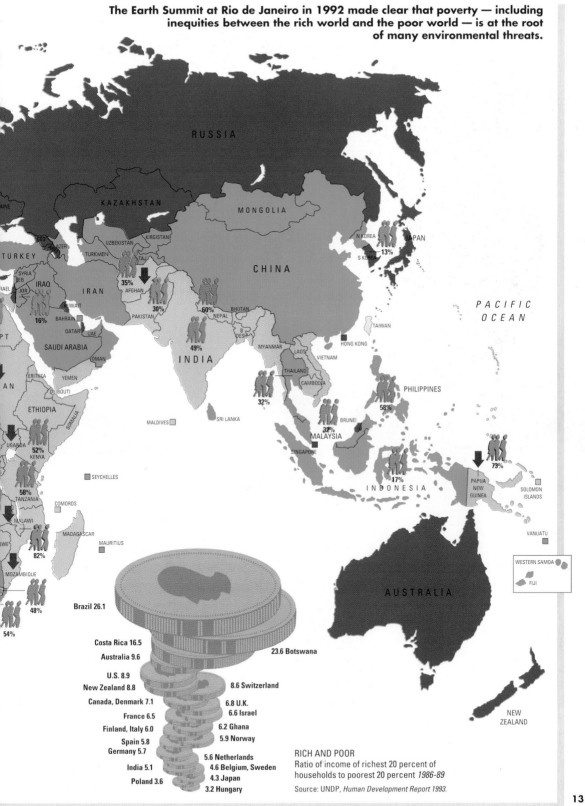

RICH AND POOR
Ratio of income of richest 20 percent of households to poorest 20 percent *1986-89*

Source: UNDP, *Human Development Report 1993.*

Brazil 26.1

23.6 Botswana

Costa Rica 16.5

Australia 9.6

U.S. 8.9
New Zealand 8.8   8.6 Switzerland

Canada, Denmark 7.1
                               6.8 U.K.
France 6.5   6.6 Israel
Finland, Italy 6.0   6.2 Ghana
Spain 5.8   5.9 Norway
Germany 5.7
                               5.6 Netherlands
India 5.1   4.6 Belgium, Sweden
                               4.3 Japan
Poland 3.6
                               3.2 Hungary

In the U.S.A., people spend 10% of their household income on food; in Ghana, they spend 50%, and in Tanzania, 64%.

CHANGES IN FOOD PRODUCTION PER CAPITA IN AFRICA
1991-92 percentages

- 5% increase
- 3%
- no change
- 3% decrease
- 5%
- 10%

- no data

- food imports increased 50% or more *1987-92*

- economies dependent on agricultural exports *1992*

- malnourished children under five years old *where known* *1990* percentages
  60

- emergency or exceptional food aid needed *1993-94*

Source: FAO.

CALORIES AVAILABLE PER CAPITA COMPARED WITH AVERAGE DAILY NEED
1989 -90 percentages
more than average

- over 30% more
- 21-30%
- 11-20%
- up to 10% more

less than average

- up to 10% less
- 10-20%
- more than 20% less

- no data

malnourished children under five years old *where known, excluding Africa 1990* percentages
13

Source: FAO.

The world's population depends on just 30 crops for 95% of its food. Four crops — wheat, rice, maize and potato — account for a bigger share than all other crops combined.

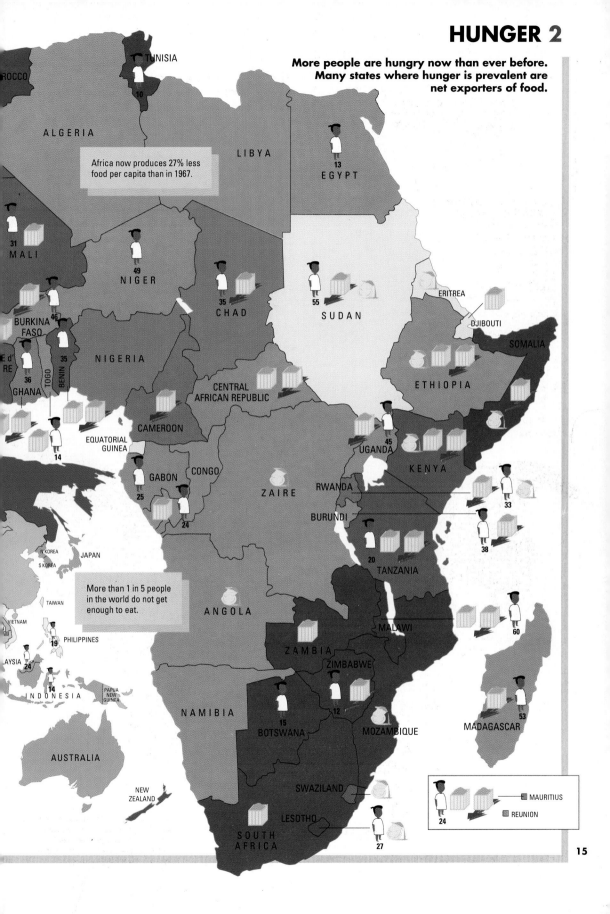

More people are hungry now than ever before. Many states where hunger is prevalent are net exporters of food.

Africa now produces 27% less food per capita than in 1967.

More than 1 in 5 people in the world do not get enough to eat.

MOROCCO

TUNISIA
10

ALGERIA

LIBYA

EGYPT
13

MALI
31

NIGER
49

CHAD
35

SUDAN
55

ERITREA

DJIBOUTI

SOMALIA

BURKINA FASO
46

Côte d'IVOIRE
36

GHANA
14

TOGO
35

BENIN
35

NIGERIA

CENTRAL AFRICAN REPUBLIC

ETHIOPIA

CAMEROON

EQUATORIAL GUINEA

GABON
25

CONGO

ZAIRE

UGANDA
45

KENYA

RWANDA

BURUNDI
24

TANZANIA
20

N KOREA

S KOREA

JAPAN

TAIWAN

VIETNAM

PHILIPPINES
19

MALAYSIA
24

INDONESIA
14

PAPUA NEW GUINEA

ANGOLA

MALAWI
60

ZAMBIA

ZIMBABWE
12

AUSTRALIA

NAMIBIA

BOTSWANA
15

MOZAMBIQUE

MADAGASCAR
53

NEW ZEALAND

SWAZILAND

LESOTHO

SOUTH AFRICA
27

33

38

MAURITIUS

REUNION
24

15

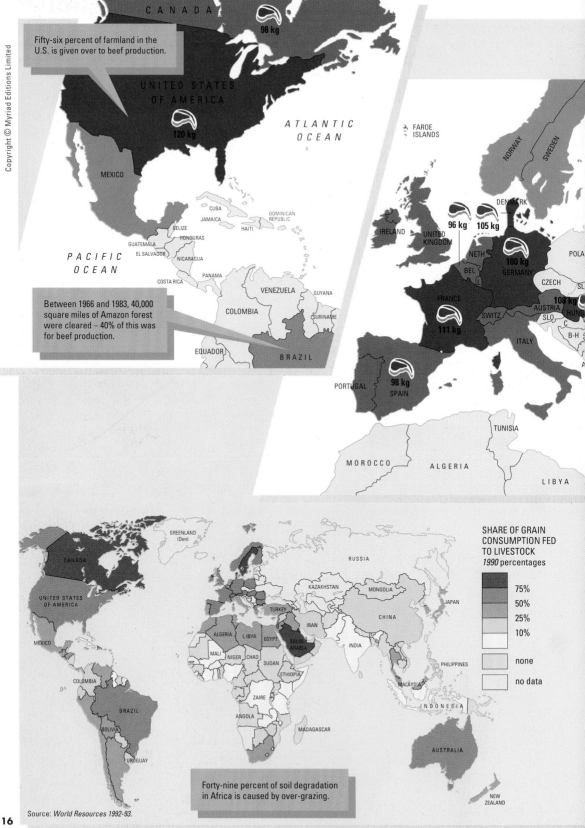

Fifty-six percent of farmland in the U.S. is given over to beef production.

98 kg

CANADA

UNITED STATES OF AMERICA

120 kg

MEXICO

ATLANTIC OCEAN

PACIFIC OCEAN

CUBA
JAMAICA
BELIZE
GUATEMALA
HONDURAS
EL SALVADOR
NICARAGUA
COSTA RICA
PANAMA

DOMINICAN REPUBLIC
HAITI

VENEZUELA
COLOMBIA
GUYANA
SURINAME

Between 1966 and 1983, 40,000 square miles of Amazon forest were cleared – 40% of this was for beef production.

EQUADOR
BRAZIL

FAROE ISLANDS

NORWAY
SWEDEN

IRELAND
UNITED KINGDOM

NETH
BEL

DENMARK
96 kg   105 kg

100 kg
GERMANY

FRANCE
SWITZ
AUSTRIA
SLO
ITALY

111 kg

POLA
CZECH
SL
108 kg
HUNG
C
B-H

PORTUGAL
SPAIN
98 kg

TUNISIA

MOROCCO
ALGERIA
LIBYA

SHARE OF GRAIN CONSUMPTION FED TO LIVESTOCK
1990 percentages

75%
50%
25%
10%
none
no data

GREENLAND (Den)

CANADA

UNITED STATES OF AMERICA

MEXICO

COLOMBIA

BRAZIL

BOLIVIA

URUGUAY

RUSSIA

KAZAKHSTAN
MONGOLIA
JAPAN

TURKEY
IRAN
CHINA

ALGERIA
LIBYA
EGYPT
SAUDI ARABIA

MALI
NIGER
CHAD
SUDAN
ETHIOPIA

INDIA

PHILIPPINES

MALAYSIA

INDONESIA

ZAIRE

ANGOLA
MADAGASCAR

AUSTRALIA

Forty-nine percent of soil degradation in Africa is caused by over-grazing.

NEW ZEALAND

Source: *World Resources 1992-93*.

THE FATTED CALF 3

Meat-eating is mostly a habit of affluence. An increasing share of world grain production is fed to livestock and many countries produce more feed grains than food grains.

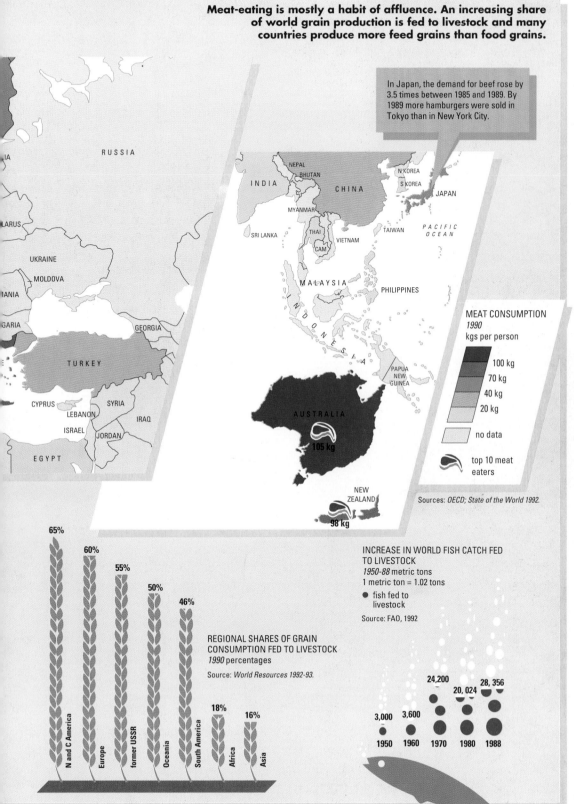

In Japan, the demand for beef rose by 3.5 times between 1985 and 1989. By 1989 more hamburgers were sold in Tokyo than in New York City.

MEAT CONSUMPTION
1990
kgs per person

- 100 kg
- 70 kg
- 40 kg
- 20 kg
- no data
- top 10 meat eaters

AUSTRALIA **105 kg**

NEW ZEALAND **98 kg**

Sources: *OECD; State of the World 1992.*

REGIONAL SHARES OF GRAIN CONSUMPTION FED TO LIVESTOCK
1990 percentages
Source: *World Resources 1992-93.*

- N and C America 65%
- Europe 60%
- former USSR 55%
- Oceania 50%
- South America 46%
- Africa 18%
- Asia 16%

INCREASE IN WORLD FISH CATCH FED TO LIVESTOCK
1950-88 metric tons
1 metric ton = 1.02 tons

● fish fed to livestock

Source: FAO, 1992

1950	1960	1970	1980	1988
3,000	3,600	24,200	20,024	28,356

17

ICELAND

NORWAY

SWEDEN

FINLAND

ESTONIA

LATVIA

LITHUANIA

DENMARK

BELAR

IRELAND

UNITED
KINGDOM

NETH

POLAND

UKRAI

BEL

GERMANY

CZECH
REPUBLIC

SLOVAK

FRANCE

SWITZ

AUSTRIA

HUNGARY

ROMAN

SLO

CROATIA

B-H

YUG

BULGAR

ITALY

ALB

M

PORTUGAL

SPAIN

GREECE

GIBRALTAR

MALTA

C A N A D A

Every year in the U.S.A., 940,000
people suffer from waterborne
dieases and 900 of them die.

UNITED STATES
OF AMERICA

MEXICO

CUBA

DOMINICAN
REPUBLIC

PUERTO RICO (US)

JAMAICA

HAITI

BELIZE

HONDURAS

GUATEMALA

EL SALVADOR

NICARAGUA

COSTA RICA

PANAMA

VENEZUELA

GUYANA

SURINAME

FRENCH GUIANA (Fr)

COLOMBIA

ECUADOR

BARBADOS

TRINIDAD & TOBAGO

A T L A N T I C
O C E A N

MOROCCO

TUNISIA

ALGERIA

LIBYA

WESTERN SAHARA

CAPE VERDE

MAURITANIA

MALI

NIGER

CHA

SENEGAL

GAMBIA

BURKINA
FASO

GUINEA-BISSAU

GUINEA

CÔTE d'
IVOIRE

BENIN

NIGERIA

SIERRA LEONE

GHANA

CAMEROON

LIBERIA

TOGO

EQUATORIAL GUINEA

GABON

ZA

SAO TOME & PRINCIPE

CONGO

ANGOLA

BRAZIL

PERU

P A C I F I C
O C E A N

BOLIVIA

PARAGUAY

CHILE

NAMIBIA

SOU
AFR

URUGUAY

ARGENTINA

FALKLAND ISLANDS
(UK)

Italy 26 gallons

PROPORTION OF POPULATION
WITHOUT ACCESS TO
SAFE DRINKING WATER
in the home or within a
15 minute walk
late 1980s or latest available
percentages

75%

50%

25%

10%

no data

ANNUAL CONSUMPTION OF
BOTTLED WATER *1993*
gallons per person

U.S. 8 gallons

Japan 0.75 gallons

Sources: WHO; UN, *Statistical Yearbook 1990-91.*

Sources: International Bottled Water Association; *Environmental Almanac.*

More than a billion people in the world lack access to safe drinking water. Sewage pollution is the biggest problem in the poor world, but industrial pollution and agricultural runoff are growing threats everywhere.

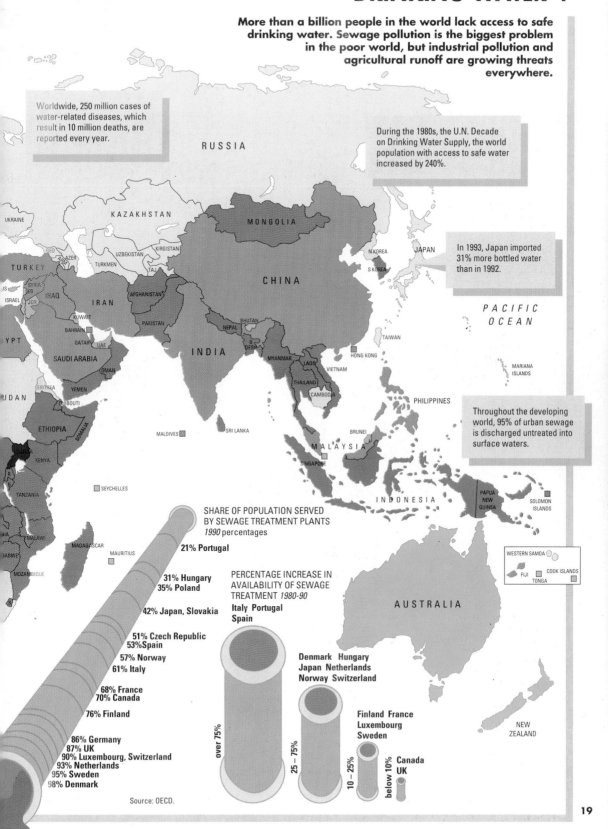

Worldwide, 250 million cases of water-related diseases, which result in 10 million deaths, are reported every year.

During the 1980s, the U.N. Decade on Drinking Water Supply, the world population with access to safe water increased by 240%.

In 1993, Japan imported 31% more bottled water than in 1992.

Throughout the developing world, 95% of urban sewage is discharged untreated into surface waters.

RUSSIA

KAZAKHSTAN

MONGOLIA

CHINA

JAPAN

N.KOREA

S.KOREA

UKRAINE

KIRGISTAN

UZBEKISTAN

TURKMEN

TAJ

AFGHANISTAN

TURKEY

GEO
AZER
SYRIA
LEB
IRAQ
ISRAEL
JOR
KUWAIT
BAHRAIN
QATAR UAE
OMAN
SAUDI ARABIA
YEMEN
DJIBOUTI
ERITREA
EGYPT
SUDAN

IRAN

PAKISTAN

NEPAL

BHUTAN

B.
DESH

INDIA

MYANMAR

THAILAND

LAOS

VIETNAM

CAMBODIA

TAIWAN

HONG KONG

PHILIPPINES

PACIFIC OCEAN

MARIANA ISLANDS

ETHIOPIA

SOMALIA

KENYA

UGANDA

TANZANIA

MADAGASCAR

MALAWI

MOZAMBIQUE

ZIMBABWE

MALDIVES

SRI LANKA

SEYCHELLES

MAURITIUS

MALAYSIA

SINGAPORE

BRUNEI

INDONESIA

PAPUA NEW GUINEA

SOLOMON ISLANDS

AUSTRALIA

WESTERN SAMOA

FIJI

TONGA

COOK ISLANDS

NEW ZEALAND

SHARE OF POPULATION SERVED BY SEWAGE TREATMENT PLANTS
1990 percentages

21% Portugal

31% Hungary
35% Poland

42% Japan, Slovakia

51% Czech Republic
53% Spain
57% Norway
61% Italy

68% France
70% Canada

76% Finland

86% Germany
87% UK
90% Luxembourg, Switzerland
93% Netherlands
95% Sweden
98% Denmark

Source: OECD.

PERCENTAGE INCREASE IN AVAILABILITY OF SEWAGE TREATMENT 1980-90

over 75%
Italy Portugal Spain

25 – 75%
Denmark Hungary Japan Netherlands Norway Switzerland

10 – 25%
Finland France Luxembourg Sweden

below 10%
Canada UK

ICELAND

NORWAY
SWEDEN
FINLAND

ESTONIA
LATVIA
LITHUANIA

DENMARK

IRELAND

UNITED
KINGDOM
NETH.
BEL.
GERMANY

POLAND

BELARUS

CZECH
REPUBLIC
SLOVAK

UKRAINE

FRANCE

SWITZ.
AUSTRIA

SLO

HUNGARY

ROMANIA

CROATIA
B - H
YUG

BULGARIA

SPAIN

ITALY

GREECE

PORTUGAL

M
ALB

MALTA

CANADA

UNITED STATES
OF AMERICA

Southern
California

Mexico City

MEXICO

ATLANTIC
OCEAN

BAHAMAS

CUBA
DOMINICAN
REPUBLIC
BELIZE JAMAICA
HONDURAS HAITI
GUATEMALA
EL SALVADOR
NICARAGUA
COSTA RICA
PANAMA

BARBADOS

MOROCCO

WESTERN SAHARA

ALGERIA

LIBYA

CAPE VERDE

MAURITANIA

MALI

NIGER

CHAD

SENEGAL
GAMBIA
GUINEA-BISSAU
GUINEA
SIERRA LEONE
CÔTE d'
IVOIRE
LIBERIA

BURKINA
FASO
GHANA
BENIN

NIGERIA

TOGO

CAMEROON

C A R

EQUATORIAL GUINEA

GABON

Z A

CONGO

VENEZUELA
GUYANA
SURINAME
FRENCH GUIANA (Fr)

COLOMBIA

ECUADOR

PACIFIC
OCEAN

BRAZIL

PERU

BOLIVIA

PARAGUAY

CHILE

URUGUAY

ARGENTINA

ANGOLA

NAMIBIA

SOUTH
AFRIC.

STATES FACING WATER SCARCITY

in 1992

by 2010 (projected)

by 2025 (projected)

other countries

region experiencing
chronic scarcity *1992*

more than 50% of surface
water flow originates abroad

DESALINATION OF WATER
1990

top 15 states

Sources: Brown; Gleick, 1992, 1993.

FALKLAND ISLANDS
(UK)

LIBYA

A growing number of states face water scarcity; the water supply for many states lies outside their own borders.

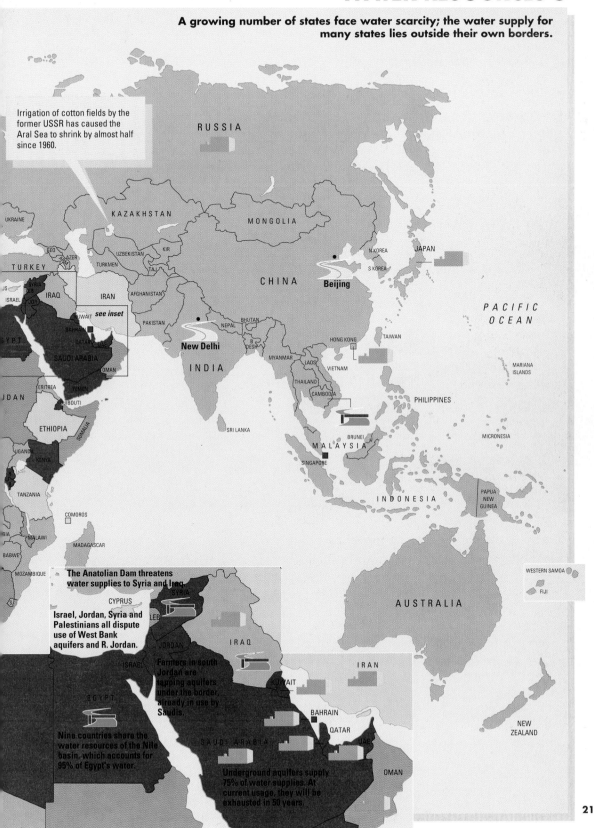

Irrigation of cotton fields by the former USSR has caused the Aral Sea to shrink by almost half since 1960.

RUSSIA

KAZAKHSTAN

MONGOLIA

UKRAINE

GEO
AZER
TURKMEN
UZBEKISTAN
KIR
TAJ

TURKEY

JS
SYRIA
LEB
ISRAEL
JOR
IRAQ

IRAN

AFGHANISTAN

KUWAIT

see inset

BAHRAIN

GYPT
QATAR
UAE

SAUDI ARABIA

OMAN

JDAN
ERITREA
YEMEN
DJIBOUTI

ETHIOPIA

SOMALIA

UGANDA
KENYA

TANZANIA

COMOROS

BIA
MALAWI

MADAGASCAR

BABWE

MOZAMBIQUE

PAKISTAN

NEPAL
BHUTAN

New Delhi

INDIA

B
DESH

MYANMAR

SRI LANKA

LAOS
VIETNAM

THAILAND

CAMBODIA

CHINA

Beijing

N.KOREA
S KOREA

JAPAN

HONG KONG
TAIWAN

PHILIPPINES

MALAYSIA

SINGAPORE

BRUNEI

MICRONESIA

PACIFIC
OCEAN

MARIANA
ISLANDS

INDONESIA

PAPUA
NEW
GUINEA

AUSTRALIA

WESTERN SAMOA

FIJI

NEW
ZEALAND

The Anatolian Dam threatens water supplies to Syria and Iraq.

CYPRUS

SYRIA

LEB

Israel, Jordan, Syria and Palestinians all dispute use of West Bank aquifers and R. Jordan.

JORDAN

ISRAEL

EGYPT

IRAQ

Farmers in south Jordan are tapping aquifers under the border, already in use by Saudis.

KUWAIT

IRAN

BAHRAIN

QATAR

UAE

Nine countries share the water resources of the Nile basin, which accounts for 95% of Egypt's water.

SAUDI ARABIA

OMAN

Underground aquifers supply 75% of water supplies. At current usage, they will be exhausted in 50 years.

By the early 1990s, 7,000 pieces of
trackable debris were orbiting the
earth – jettisoned during 30 years
of space missions. Each year, they
are joined by another 400.

Source: press report

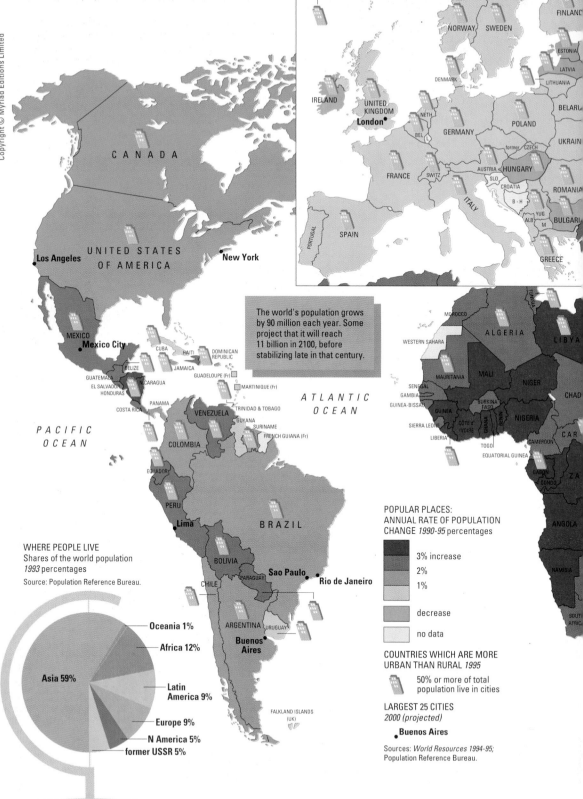

ICELAND

FINLAND

NORWAY SWEDEN

ESTONIA

DENMARK

LATVIA

LITHUANIA

IRELAND

UNITED
KINGDOM
London •

NETH.

BELARUS

BEL.

POLAND

UKRAINE

GERMANY

former CZECH

FRANCE SWITZ.

AUSTRIA HUNGARY

ROMANIA

SLO

CROATIA

B - H

YUG

M

BULGARIA

ALB

PORTUGAL

SPAIN

ITALY

GREECE

C A N A D A

Los Angeles •

UNITED STATES
OF AMERICA

• **New York**

MOROCCO

WESTERN SAHARA

ALGERIA

LIBYA

MEXICO

Mexico City

CUBA HAITI

DOMINICAN
REPUBLIC

BELIZE

JAMAICA

GUADELOUPE (Fr)

GUATEMALA

EL SALVADOR
HONDURAS

NICARAGUA

MARTINIQUE (Fr)

PANAMA

COSTA RICA

TRINIDAD & TOBAGO

VENEZUELA

GUYANA

SURINAME

FRENCH GUIANA (Fr)

COLOMBIA

MAURITANIA

MALI

NIGER

SENEGAL

GAMBIA

GUINEA-BISSAU

GUINEA

BURKINA
FASO

BENIN

NIGERIA

SIERRA LEONE

CÔTE d'
IVOIRE

GHANA

LIBERIA

TOGO

CAMEROON

EQUATORIAL GUINEA

CHAD

CAR

The world's population grows
by 90 million each year. Some
project that it will reach
11 billion in 2100, before
stabilizing late in that century.

A T L A N T I C
O C E A N

P A C I F I C
O C E A N

ECUADOR

PERU

Lima •

B R A Z I L

GABON

CONGO

ZA

ANGOLA

POPULAR PLACES:
ANNUAL RATE OF POPULATION
CHANGE *1990-95* percentages

BOLIVIA

PARAGUAY

Sao Paulo •

Rio de Janeiro

CHILE

3% increase

2%

1%

WHERE PEOPLE LIVE
Shares of the world population
1993 percentages

Source: Population Reference Bureau.

ARGENTINA

URUGUAY

**Buenos
Aires** •

decrease

no data

NAMIBIA

SOUTH
AFRICA

Oceania 1%

Africa 12%

Asia 59%

Latin
America 9%

Europe 9%

N America 5%

former USSR 5%

FALKLAND ISLANDS
(UK)

COUNTRIES WHICH ARE MORE
URBAN THAN RURAL *1995*

50% or more of total
population live in cities

LARGEST 25 CITIES
2000 (projected)

• **Buenos Aires**

Sources: *World Resources 1994-95;*
Population Reference Bureau.

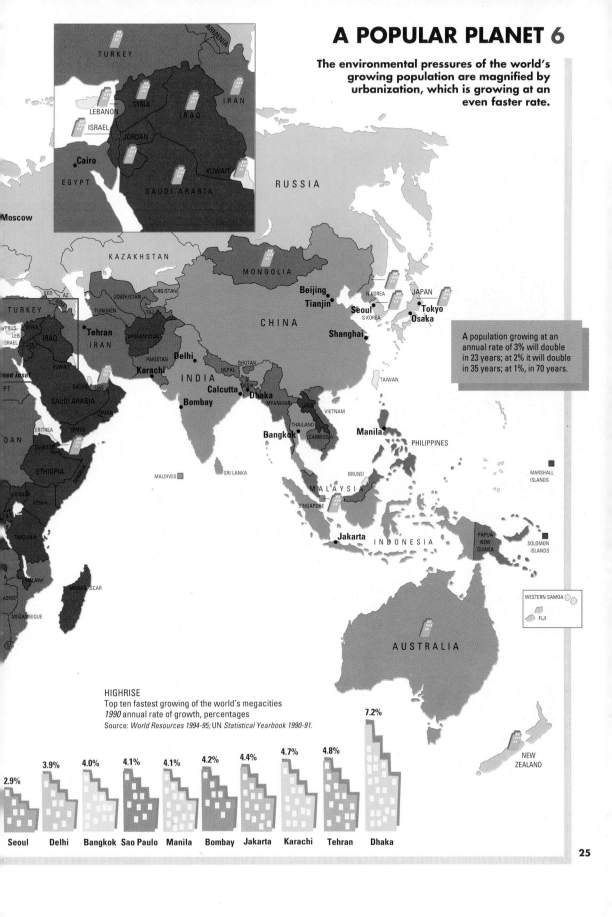

A POPULAR PLANET 6

The environmental pressures of the world's growing population are magnified by urbanization, which is growing at an even faster rate.

A population growing at an annual rate of 3% will double in 23 years; at 2% it will double in 35 years; at 1%, in 70 years.

HIGHRISE
Top ten fastest growing of the world's megacities
1990 annual rate of growth, percentages
Source: *World Resources 1994-95;* UN *Statistical Yearbook 1990-91.*

Seoul	2.9%
Delhi	3.9%
Bangkok	4.0%
Sao Paulo	4.1%
Manila	4.1%
Bombay	4.2%
Jakarta	4.4%
Karachi	4.7%
Tehran	4.8%
Dhaka	7.2%

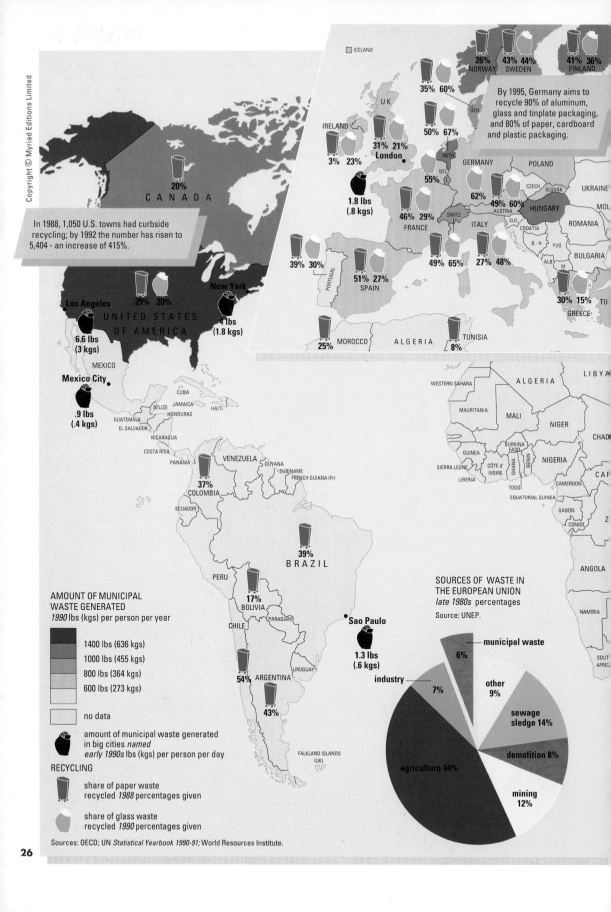

ICELAND

26% NORWAY   43% 44% SWEDEN   41% 36% FINLAND

35% 60% DEN

By 1995, Germany aims to recycle 90% of aluminum, glass and tinplate packaging, and 80% of paper, cardboard and plastic packaging.

UK

IRELAND

31% 21% London

3% 23%

50% 67%

NETH

GERMANY   POLAND

BEL   CZECH   SLOVAK   UKRAINE

55%

1.8 lbs (.8 kgs)

62%   49% 60% HUNGARY   MOL

46% 29% FRANCE   SWITZ   AUSTRIA   SLO   ROMANIA

CROATIA

ITALY   B - H   YUG

49% 65%   27% 48%   ALB   M   BULGARIA

39% 30%

PORTUGAL

51% 27% SPAIN

30% 15% GREECE   TU

25% MOROCCO   ALGERIA   TUNISIA   8%

20% C A N A D A

In 1988, 1,050 U.S. towns had curbside recycling; by 1992 the number has risen to 5,404 - an increase of 415%.

New York

29% 20%

Los Angeles   U N I T E D   S T A T E S   4 lbs (1.8 kgs)

O F   A M E R I C A

6.6 lbs (3 kgs)

MEXICO

Mexico City

.9 lbs (.4 kgs)

CUBA

BELIZE   JAMAICA   HAITI

GUATEMALA   HONDURAS

EL SALVADOR

NICARAGUA

COSTA RICA

PANAMA   VENEZUELA   GUYANA

SURINAME

FRENCH GUIANA (Fr)

37% COLOMBIA

ECUADOR

39% B R A Z I L

PERU

17% BOLIVIA

PARAGUAY   Sao Paulo

CHILE   1.3 lbs (.6 kgs)

URUGUAY

54% ARGENTINA

43%

FALKLAND ISLANDS (UK)

LIBYA

WESTERN SAHARA   ALGERIA

MAURITANIA   MALI   NIGER   CHAD

GUINEA   BURKINA FASO   NIGERIA   CAF

SIERRA LEONE   CÔTE d'IVOIRE   GHANA   BENIN   CAMEROON

LIBERIA   TOGO

EQUATORIAL GUINEA   GABON

CONGO

ANGOLA

NAMIBIA   SOUT AFRIC

AMOUNT OF MUNICIPAL WASTE GENERATED
1990 lbs (kgs) per person per year

- 1400 lbs (636 kgs)
- 1000 lbs (455 kgs)
- 800 lbs (364 kgs)
- 600 lbs (273 kgs)
- no data

amount of municipal waste generated in big cities *named* *early 1990s* lbs (kgs) per person per day

RECYCLING

share of paper waste recycled *1988* percentages given

share of glass waste recycled *1990* percentages given

SOURCES OF WASTE IN THE EUROPEAN UNION
late 1980s percentages
Source: UNEP.

municipal waste 6%

other 9%

industry 7%

sewage sledge 14%

demolition 8%

agriculture 44%

mining 12%

Sources: OECD; UN *Statistical Yearbook 1990-91;* World Resources Institute.

Rich countries and rich people generate more waste than poor countries and poor people. There are few good waste disposal options.

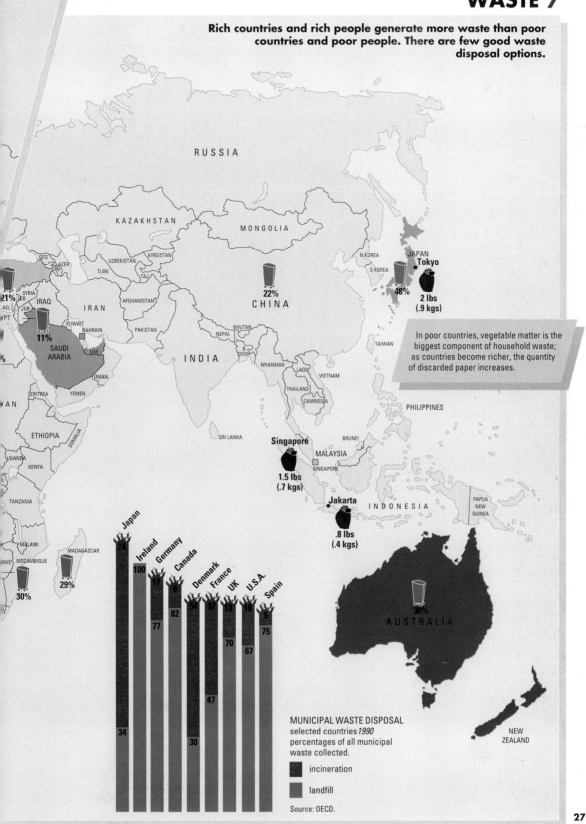

In poor countries, vegetable matter is the biggest component of household waste; as countries become richer, the quantity of discarded paper increases.

RUSSIA

KAZAKHSTAN

MONGOLIA

22%

CHINA

JAPAN
Tokyo

48%

2 lbs
(.9 kgs)

21%

11%

SAUDI
ARABIA

IRAN

INDIA

TAIWAN

MYANMAR

LAOS

THAILAND

VIETNAM

CAMBODIA

PHILIPPINES

SRI LANKA

Singapore

MALAYSIA

SINGAPORE

BRUNEI

1.5 lbs
(.7 kgs)

Jakarta

INDONESIA

PAPUA
NEW
GUINEA

.8 lbs
(.4 kgs)

ETHIOPIA

29%

30%

AUSTRALIA

30%

NEW
ZEALAND

MUNICIPAL WASTE DISPOSAL
selected countries *1990*
percentages of all municipal
waste collected.

■ incineration

■ landfill

Source: OECD.

Japan — 74 / 34
Ireland — 100
Germany — 17 / 77
Canada — 9 / 82
Denmark — 54 / 47
France — 37 / 30
UK — 13 / 70
U.S.A. — 16 / 67
Spain — 9 / 75

Airborne lead levels in central London dropped by 90% in the decade of the 1980s.

ICELAND

FINLA

NORWAY

SWEDEN

Helsinki

DENMARK

ESTONIA

LATVI

Copenhagen

Glasgow

LITHUANIA

IRELAND

UNITED
KINGDOM

Dublin

London

Amsterdam

GERMANY

NETH.

Frankfurt

POLAND

Warsaw

BELAR

Wraclow

CZECH
REPUBLIC

UKRA

Brussels

FRANCE

AUSTRIA

S

SWITZ

Munich

SLO

HUNGARY

ROMAN

Gourdon

B - H

CRO

YUG

Madrid

ITALY

Milan

Zagreb

ALB

M

BULGA

PORTUGAL

Lisbon

SPAIN

Athens

GREECE

CANADA

Vancouver

UNITED STATES
OF AMERICA

Montreal

Toronto

Hamilton

Chicago

New York

Los Angeles

MEXICO

Mexico
City

ATLANTIC
OCEAN

MOROCCO

TUNISIA

ALGERIA

LIBYA

CUBA

JAMAICA

DOMINICAN
REPUBLIC

PUERTO RICO (US)

WESTERN SAHARA

BELIZE

HONDURAS

HAITI

GUATEMALA

EL
SALVADOR

NICARAGUA

MAURITANIA

MALI

NIGER

CAPE VERDE

SENEGAL

GAMBIA

COSTA RICA

PANAMA

VENEZUELA

GUYANA

GUINEA-BISSAU

GUINEA

BURKINA
FASO

CHA

Medellin

COLOMBIA

Cali

Caracas

SURINAME

FRENCH GUIANA (Fr)

SIERRA LEONE

CÔTE d'
IVOIRE

GHANA

BENIN

NIGERIA

ECUADOR

LIBERIA

TOGO

CAMEROON

C

EQUATORIAL GUINEA

SAO TOME & PRINCIPE

GABON

CONGO

Z

**159
Los
Angeles**

**UNHEALTHY
AIR DAYS**
1992
**26 worst U.S.
metropolitan areas**

PERU

BRAZIL

BOLIVIA

Rio de Janeiro

ANGOLA

NAMIBIA

CHILE

PARAGUAY

Sao Paolo

ARGENTINA

Santiago

URUGUAY

46 Bakersfield

40 Houston

35 El Paso
33 Fresno

29 Sacramento
27 San Diego

New York 26

24 Philadelphia

New Haven 21

20 Washington D.C.
18 Salt Lake City

13 Las Vegas

Detroit 11
San Francisco 9

Atlanta, Phoenix 6

10 Milwaukee, Providence
8 Chicago, Cincinnati
7 Baton Rouge, Hartford, St. Louis, Grand Rapids, Denver

Buenos Aires

FALKLAND ISLANDS
(UK)

Source: *Environmental Almanac 1994.*

28

Regions of poor air quality
Source: *Earth Journal.*

In many cities, just breathing is a health hazard.

URBAN AIR POLLUTION
early 1990s where known

sulphur ___ nitrogen
dioxide   dioxide
dust

severe pollution: WHO guidelines
exceeded by factor of 2

moderate pollution: WHO guidelines
exceeded by less than factor of 2

low pollution: WHO guidelines
usually met

no data

serious lead pollution

**SEVERE URBAN POLLUTION IN
STATES OF THE FORMER USSR**
late 1980s

benzopyrene ___ nitrogen
               dioxide
dust

benzopyrene

dust

nitrogen dioxide

no data

Sources: UNEP; WHO; GEMS; Elsom; *Earth Journal;*
Feshbach & Friendly; Peterson; *World Resources 1990-91.*

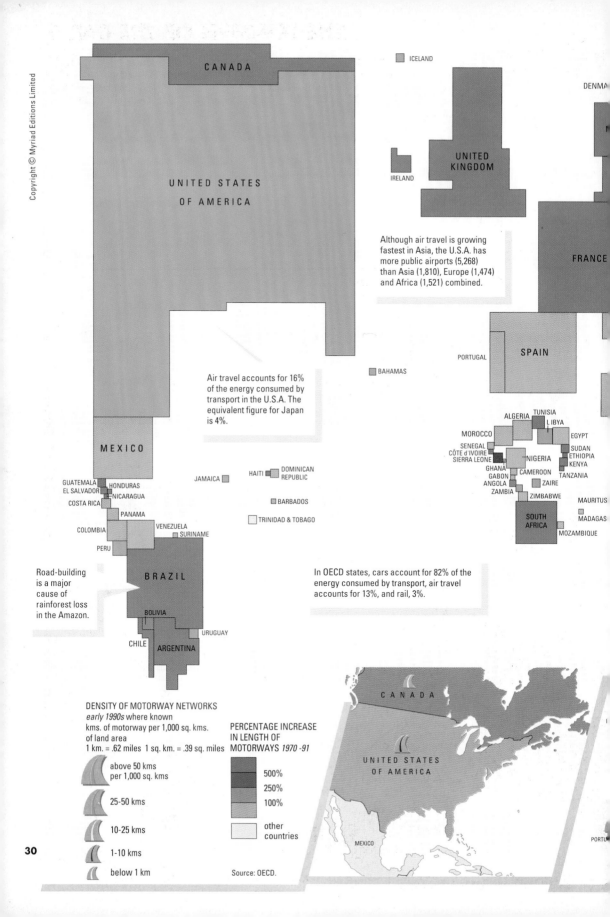

Copyright © Myriad Editions Limited

CANADA

ICELAND

DENMA...

UNITED KINGDOM

IRELAND

UNITED STATES OF AMERICA

FRANCE

Although air travel is growing fastest in Asia, the U.S.A. has more public airports (5,268) than Asia (1,810), Europe (1,474) and Africa (1,521) combined.

SPAIN

PORTUGAL

BAHAMAS

Air travel accounts for 16% of the energy consumed by transport in the U.S.A. The equivalent figure for Japan is 4%.

ALGERIA   TUNISIA
           LIBYA
MOROCCO   EGYPT
SENEGAL   SUDAN
CÔTE d'IVOIRE   ETHIOPIA
SIERRA LEONE   NIGERIA KENYA
GHANA
GABON   CAMEROON   TANZANIA
ANGOLA   ZAIRE
ZAMBIA   MAURITUS
        ZIMBABWE
                      MADAGAS...
SOUTH   MOZAMBIQUE
AFRICA

MEXICO

GUATEMALA
EL SALVADOR   HONDURAS
              NICARAGUA
COSTA RICA
        PANAMA

COLOMBIA   VENEZUELA
           SURINAME
PERU

JAMAICA   HAITI   DOMINICAN REPUBLIC

BARBADOS

TRINIDAD & TOBAGO

Road-building is a major cause of rainforest loss in the Amazon.

BRAZIL

In OECD states, cars account for 82% of the energy consumed by transport, air travel accounts for 13%, and rail, 3%.

BOLIVIA

URUGUAY

CHILE   ARGENTINA

DENSITY OF MOTORWAY NETWORKS
early 1990s where known
kms. of motorway per 1,000 sq. kms.
of land area
1 km. = .62 miles 1 sq. km. = .39 sq. miles

PERCENTAGE INCREASE IN LENGTH OF MOTORWAYS 1970 -91

above 50 kms per 1,000 sq. kms

25-50 kms

10-25 kms

1-10 kms

below 1 km

500%
250%
100%
other countries

Source: OECD.

CANADA

UNITED STATES OF AMERICA

MEXICO

PORTU...

30

The real price of car dependence includes accidents, congestion, pollution, noise, and the environmental destruction caused by road building. Air travel, growing rapidly, has its own environmental costs.

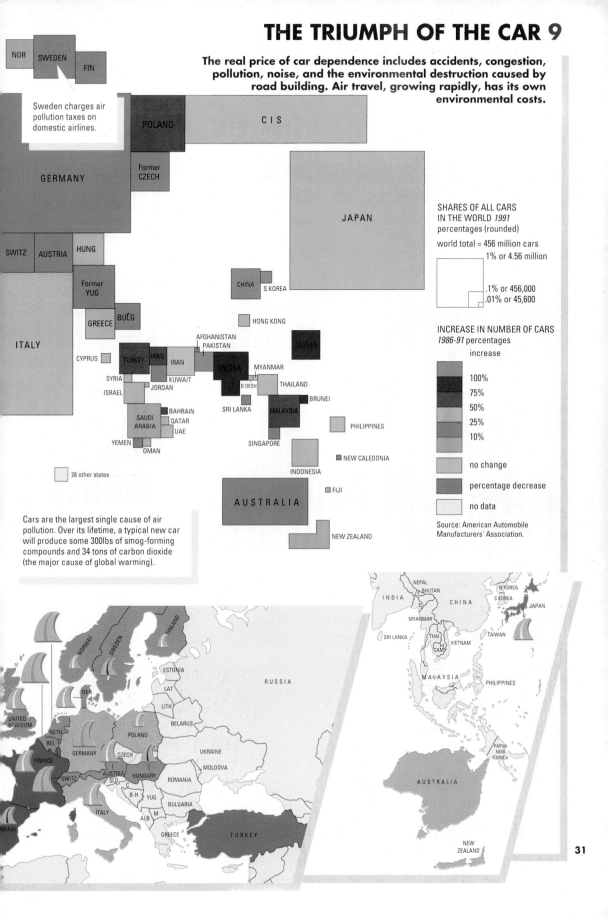

NOR

SWEDEN

FIN

Sweden charges air pollution taxes on domestic airlines.

POLAND

CIS

Former CZECH

GERMANY

JAPAN

SWITZ   AUSTRIA   HUNG

Former YUG

CHINA   S KOREA

BULG

GREECE

HONG KONG

ITALY

AFGHANISTAN
PAKISTAN

TAIWAN

CYPRUS

TURKEY   IRAQ   IRAN

INDIA

MYANMAR

SYRIA   KUWAIT

THAILAND

ISRAEL   JORDAN

B DESH

SRI LANKA

BRUNEI

BAHRAIN

SAUDI   QATAR
ARABIA   UAE

MALAYSIA

YEMEN

PHILIPPINES

OMAN

SINGAPORE

NEW CALEDONIA

INDONESIA

28 other states

FIJI

AUSTRALIA

NEW ZEALAND

SHARES OF ALL CARS IN THE WORLD *1991*
percentages (rounded)

world total = 456 million cars

1% or 4.56 million

.1% or 456,000
.01% or 45,600

INCREASE IN NUMBER OF CARS
1986-91 percentages

increase

100%

75%

50%

25%

10%

no change

percentage decrease

no data

Source: American Automobile Manufacturers' Association.

Cars are the largest single cause of air pollution. Over its lifetime, a typical new car will produce some 300lbs of smog-forming compounds and 34 tons of carbon dioxide (the major cause of global warming).

NORWAY

SWEDEN

FINLAND

NEPAL

BHUTAN

N KOREA
S KOREA

INDIA

CHINA

JAPAN

MYANMAR

SRI LANKA

THAI

VIETNAM

TAIWAN

CAM

ESTONIA

RUSSIA

MALAYSIA

PHILIPPINES

DEN

LAT

LITH

UNITED KINGDOM

BELARUS

NETH

POLAND

PAPUA NEW GUINEA

BEL

GERMANY

CZECH

UKRAINE

FRANCE

AUSTRIA
SLO

HUNGARY

MOLDOVA

SWITZ

B-H

YUG

ROMANIA

AUSTRALIA

ITALY

ALB

BULGARIA

M

SPAIN

GREECE

TURKEY

NEW ZEALAND

Between 1988 and 1992, worldwide consumption of CFCs fell by 40%.

-57% ICELAND

-79% SWEDEN

FINLAND

ESTON

LATV

LITHUANIA **-52%**

BELA

POLAND **-68%**

UKRA

CZECH **-80%** **-51%** SLOVAK

EUROPEAN UNION **-53%**

-60% **-70%** AUSTRIA HUNGARY

SWITZ. SLO **-55%** **-28%**

B - H YUG ROMANI

ALB M BULGAR

-37%

-67% MALTA

GREENLAND (Den)

C A N A D A **-51%**

UNITED STATES OF AMERICA **-51%**

+48% MEXICO

+10% **+28%** BAHAMAS

CUBA

BELIZE DOMINICAN REPUBLIC

HONDURAS JAMAICA PUERTO RICO (US)

GUATEMALA **+165%**

EL SALVADOR

NICARAGUA

COSTA RICA **+75%**

PANAMA VENEZUELA **-21%** GUYANA

-38% SURINAME FRENCH GUIANA (Fr)

COLOMBIA

-27% ECUADOR

-22%

PERU B R A Z I L

BOLIVIA

CHILE PARAGUAY

+16%

URUGUAY **-21%**

ARGENTINA

A T L A N T I C O C E A N

P A C I F I C O C E A N

+80% TUNISIA **+300%** CYPRUS SYRIA IRAN **+122%**

MOROCCO ISRAEL **-8%** JOR IRAQ KUWAIT

ALGERIA LIBYA **-79%** BAHRAIN

WESTERN SAHARA EGYPT QATAR

SAUDI ARAB

MAURITANIA MALI NIGER

SENEGAL CHAD S U D A N ERITREA YEMEN

GAMBIA BURKINA DJIBOUTI

GUINEA-BISSAU GUINEA FASO BENIN NIGERIA

SIERRA LEONE CÔTE D' GHANA CAR ETHIOPIA SOMALIA

LIBERIA IVOIRE

+59% TOGO CAMEROON **+43%**

+18% EQUATORIAL U KENYA

GUINEA GABON CONGO ZAIRE R **+24**

+78% **-30%** TANZANIA

COMOROS

A N G O L A ZAMBIA MALAWI MADAGAS

ZIMBAB **+105%**

NAMIBIA BOTSWANA MOZAMBIQUE

-35% SOUTH AFRICA

The ozone-layer hole over Antarctica was 13 times wider in 1991 than in 1981.

halon 1301
fire extinguishers
110 years

methyl chloroform
solvents

carbon tetrachloride
solvents
67 years

5% 8%

4%

12%
CFC-113
solvents 90 years

45% **CFC-12**
aerosols, foams,
refrigeration,
air conditioning

26% **CFC-11**
aerosols, foams,
refrigeration
74 years

THE OZONE KILLERS
Percentage contribution
to ozone loss, commercial uses
and length of life in atmosphere

Source: UNEP.

OZONE DECLINE
Average ozone loss over the years
1978-91 (December-March)
percentages.

Source: UNEP.

0%

-1% -2% -3%

-4%

-6% -7%

-4% -3% -2%

-1%

0%

0%

-1%

-2%

-3%

-4%

-5%

-6%

-7%

The Montreal Protocol has begun to cut the use of CFCs — but those already released will go on damaging the ozone layer for decades.

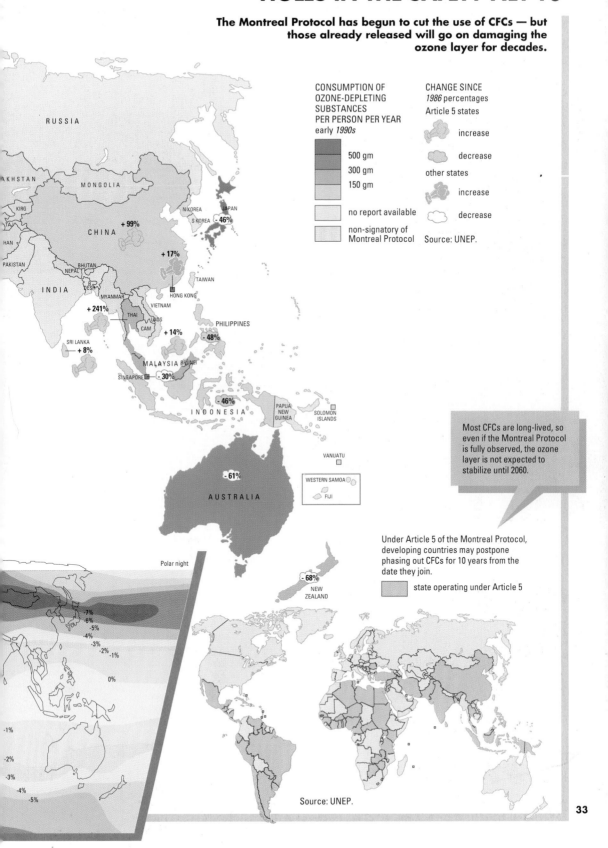

CONSUMPTION OF
OZONE-DEPLETING
SUBSTANCES
PER PERSON PER YEAR
early *1990s*

- 500 gm
- 300 gm
- 150 gm
- no report available
- non-signatory of Montreal Protocol

CHANGE SINCE
1986 percentages
Article 5 states

- increase
- decrease

other states

- increase
- decrease

Source: UNEP.

RUSSIA

AKHSTAN
MONGOLIA
KIRG
TAJ
HAN
CHINA   +99%
PAKISTAN
NEPAL
BHUTAN
INDIA   +241%
SRI LANKA   +8%
N KOREA
S KOREA   -46%
JAPAN
+17%
TAIWAN
HONG KONG
MYANMAR
VIETNAM
THAI
LAOS
CAM   +14%
PHILIPPINES   -48%
MALAYSIA   BRUNEI
SINGAPORE   -30%
INDONESIA   -46%
PAPUA NEW GUINEA
SOLOMON ISLANDS
VANUATU
WESTERN SAMOA
FIJI

AUSTRALIA   -61%

NEW ZEALAND   -68%

Polar night

-7%
-6%
-5%
-4%
-3%
-2% -1%
0%
-1%
-2%
-3%
-4%
-5%

Most CFCs are long-lived, so even if the Montreal Protocol is fully observed, the ozone layer is not expected to stabilize until 2060.

Under Article 5 of the Montreal Protocol, developing countries may postpone phasing out CFCs for 10 years from the date they join.

- state operating under Article 5

Source: UNEP.

Copyright © Myriad Editions Limited

Most tourists come from the developed world, 70% of them from just 10 countries.

ICELAND
NORWAY
SWEDEN
FINLAND
ESTONIA
LATVIA
LITHUANIA
DENMARK
IRELAND
UNITED KINGDOM
Canterbury Cathedral
NETH
BEL
L
GERMANY
POLAND
BELAR
Stonehenge
CZECH REPUBLIC
UKRA
Notre Dame
FRANCE
SWITZ
AUSTRIA
SLO
HUNGARY
SLOVAK
Alps
Carpathia Mountain
ROMANI
ITALY
CROATIA
B - H
YUG
Venice
Pisa
ALB
M
BULGA
Pyrenees
Sistine Chapel
Parthenon
PORTUGAL
SPAIN
Sardinia
GREECE
Mediterranean

Arctic Canada

CANADA

Yellowstone Park

UNITED STATES OF AMERICA

TUNISIA
Canary Islands
MOROCCO
ALGERIA
LIBYA

Florida
MEXICO
BAHAMAS
Baja California
CUBA
DOMINICAN REPUBLIC
PUERTO RICO (US)
Yucatan
BELIZE
JAMAICA
ANTIGUA & BARBUDA
GUATEMALA
HONDURAS
HAITI
EL SALVADOR
Caribbean
NICARAGUA
GRENADA
COSTA RICA
VENEZUELA
PANAMA
GUYANA
COLOMBIA
SURINAME

Millions of tourists visit the Caribbean each year. Sewage poisons mangroves and coastal waters, boats and divers damage coral reefs, and natural habitat is destroyed by building development.

MALI
NIGER
CHA
BURKINA FASO
CÔTE d' IVOIRE
GHANA
BENIN
NIGERIA
LIBERIA
TOGO
CAMEROON
EQUATORIAL GUINEA
GABON
CONGO
Z

HAWAII

Galapagos Is
ECUADOR
Amazon
Machu Picchu
BRAZIL
PERU
BOLIVIA
PARAGUAY
CHILE
ARGENTINA
URUGUAY

ANGOLA

NAMIBIA

WHERE THE TOURISTS COME FROM *1991*

top 10 tourist origin countries

other

DAMAGE CAUSED BY TOURISM
selected examples and sites

cultural sites damaged by volume of tourists

sewage and other waste pollution

deforestation

ecosystem and/ or habitats damaged

overbuilding

ECOTOURISM *1994*

current destinations

emerging destinations

Patagonia

FALKLAND ISLANDS (UK)

Golf courses springing up for Japanese, European and North American tourists are heavy users of water resources, pesticides, soil coagulants, and even coloring agents. Many have displaced local people or valuable wildlife habitat.

Sources: UN *Statistical Yearbook 1990-91; Travel and Tourism 1992; Yearbook of Tourism Statistics 1993; The Independent* (London); Geffen & Berglie; Boo; Tourism Concern, London.

ANTARCTICA

Travel is now the world's largest industry. The irony of tourism is that it often destroys some of the very places tourists travel to see.

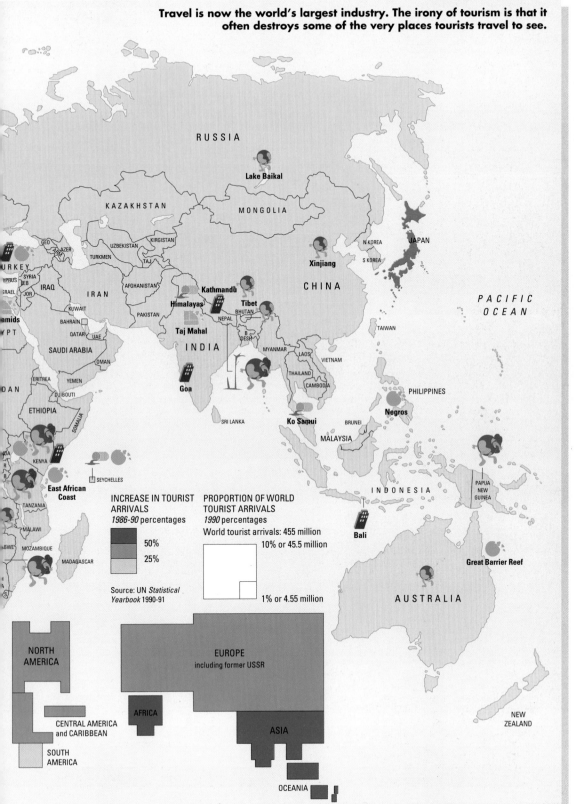

RUSSIA

Lake Baikal

KAZAKHSTAN

MONGOLIA

N KOREA

JAPAN

S KOREA

UZBEKISTAN KIRGISTAN

GEO AZER

TURKMEN TAJ.

Xinjiang

CHINA

PACIFIC
OCEAN

URKEY

SYRIA
DEB
RAEL JOR

CYPRUS

IRAQ

IRAN

AFGHANISTAN

Kathmandu

Tibet

KUWAIT

PAKISTAN

Himalayas

BHUTAN

NEPAL

TAIWAN

amids

BAHRAIN

QATAR UAE

Taj Mahal

B
DESH

P T

SAUDI ARABIA

OMAN

INDIA

MYANMAR

LAOS

VIETNAM

ERITREA YEMEN

THAILAND

DAN

DJIBOUTI

Goa

CAMBODIA

PHILIPPINES

ETHIOPIA

SRI LANKA

Ko Samui

Negros

KENYA

BRUNEI

MALAYSIA

SEYCHELLES

East African
Coast

INDONESIA

PAPUA
NEW
GUINEA

TANZANIA

**INCREASE IN TOURIST
ARRIVALS**
1986-90 percentages

**PROPORTION OF WORLD
TOURIST ARRIVALS**
1990 percentages
World tourist arrivals: 455 million

MALAWI

10% or 45.5 million

Bali

BWE

MOZAMBIQUE

50%

MADAGASCAR

25%

Great Barrier Reef

Source: UN *Statistical
Yearbook* 1990-91

1% or 4.55 million

AUSTRALIA

NORTH
AMERICA

EUROPE
including former USSR

CENTRAL AMERICA
and CARIBBEAN

AFRICA

NEW
ZEALAND

SOUTH
AMERICA

ASIA

OCEANIA

1970
3,752
million tons oil equivalent

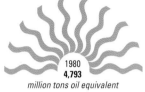

1980
4,793
million tons oil equivalent

1990
5,571
million tons oil equivalent

INCREASE IN WORLD
COMMERCIAL ENERGY CONSUMPTION

Source: OECD 1993

ICELAND

NORWAY
SWEDEN
FINLAND
DENMARK
IRELAND
UNITED
KINGDOM
NETH
BEL
GERMANY
POLAND
former
CZECH
FRANCE
AUSTRIA
HUNGARY
SWITZ
SLO
ROMANI
CROATIA
ITALY
B-H
YUG
BULGAR
ALB
M
PORTUGAL
SPAIN
GREECE
MALTA

C A N A D A

UNITED STATES
OF AMERICA

MEXICO

ATLANTIC
OCEAN

CUBA
JAMAICA
BELIZE
HONDURAS
GUATEMALA
EL SALVADOR
NICARAGUA
COSTA RICA
PANAMA
DOMINICAN
REPUBLIC
HAITI
PUERTO RICO (US)
GUADELOUPE (Fr)
MARTINIQUE (Fr)
TRINIDAD & TOBAGO
GUYANA
SURINAME
FRENCH GUIANA (Fr)

VENEZUELA
COLOMBIA
ECUADOR

PACIFIC
OCEAN

MOROCCO
WESTERN SAHARA
ALGERIA
LIBYA
TUNISIA

CAPE VERDE
MAURITANIA
MALI
NIGER
CHA
SENEGAL
GAMBIA
GUINEA-BISSAU
GUINEA
BURKINA
FASO
BENIN
NIGERIA
SIERRA LEONE
CÔTE d'
IVOIRE
GHANA
LIBERIA
TOGO
EQUATORIAL
GUINEA
CAMEROON
CA
SAO TOME & PRINCIPE
GABON
ZA
CONGO

ANGOLA

B R A Z I L

PERU

BOLIVIA

PARAGUAY

CHILE

URUGUAY

ARGENTINA

NAMIBIA

SOU
AFRI

FALKLAND ISLANDS
(UK)

Each person in the industrialized
world uses as much commercial
energy as 10 people in the
developing world.

ENERGY USE PER CAPITA COMPARED WITH WORLD AVERAGE 1989 percentages

world average (100%) = 67 gigajoules
per person per year

less than average

- 25%
- 50%

about average

- 95% - 105%

more than average

- 200%
- 300%
- 500%

- no data

CHANGES IN ENERGY CONSUMPTION 1979-89 percentages

more than 50% increase

decrease

Source: World Resources 1992-93.

CONSUMPTION OF WORLD COMMERCIAL ENERGY 1992

hydro 2%
nuclear 7%
oil 40%
gas 23%
coal 28%

Source: BP Statistical Review of
World Energy 1993.

Industrialized states use most of the world's commercial energy, but energy demands in developing countries are expected to triple by 2025.

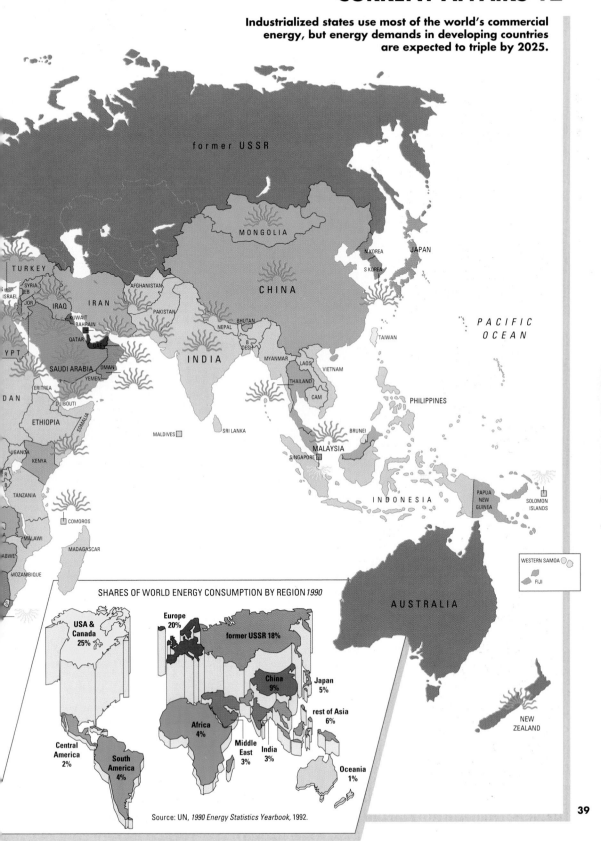

former USSR

MONGOLIA

N KOREA

JAPAN

S KOREA

TURKEY

SYRIA
DEB

ISRAEL
JOR

AFGHANISTAN

IRAQ

IRAN

PAKISTAN

KUWAIT
BAHRAIN

QATAR

UAE

OMAN

SAUDI ARABIA

YEMEN

YPT

DAN

ERITREA

DJIBOUTI

ETHIOPIA

SOMALIA

UGANDA

KENYA

TANZANIA

MALAWI

ABWE

MOZAMBIQUE

COMOROS

MADAGASCAR

CHINA

BHUTAN

NEPAL

B DESH

INDIA

MYANMAR

LAOS

THAILAND

VIETNAM

CAM

MALDIVES

SRI LANKA

BRUNEI

MALAYSIA

SINGAPORE

TAIWAN

PHILIPPINES

PACIFIC OCEAN

INDONESIA

PAPUA NEW GUINEA

SOLOMON ISLANDS

AUSTRALIA

WESTERN SAMOA

FIJI

NEW ZEALAND

SHARES OF WORLD ENERGY CONSUMPTION BY REGION 1990

USA & Canada 25%

Europe 20%

former USSR 18%

China 9%

Japan 5%

rest of Asia 6%

Africa 4%

Central America 2%

South America 4%

Middle East 3%

India 3%

Oceania 1%

Source: UN, *1990 Energy Statistics Yearbook*, 1992.

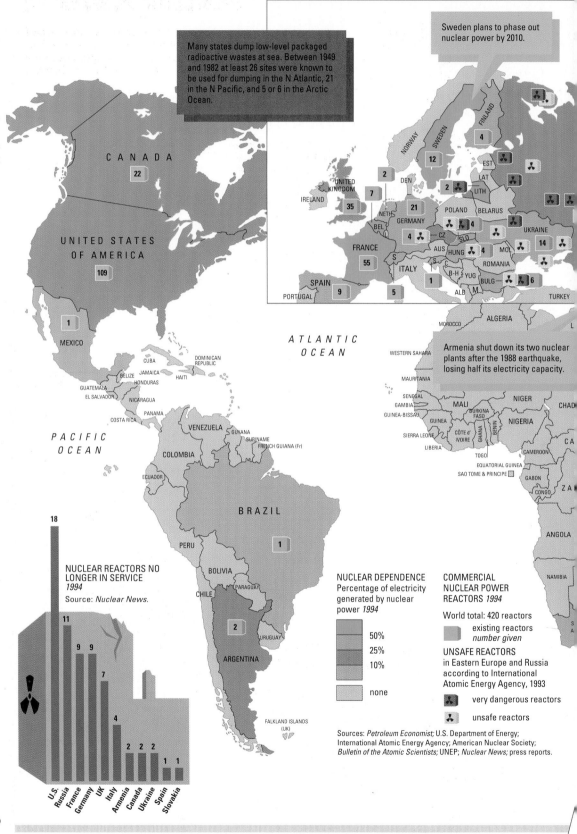

Copyright © Myriad Editions Limited

Many states dump low-level packaged radioactive wastes at sea. Between 1949 and 1982 at least 26 sites were known to be used for dumping in the N Atlantic, 21 in the N Pacific, and 5 or 6 in the Arctic Ocean.

Sweden plans to phase out nuclear power by 2010.

CANADA
22

UNITED STATES OF AMERICA
109

NORWAY SWEDEN FINLAND
12
4

UNITED KINGDOM
IRELAND
35
2
DEN
7
NETH
BEL
GERMANY
21
POLAND
BELARUS
4
4
UKRAINE
14
CZ
4
FRANCE
55
AUS HUNG
4
MOL
S
C
ROMANIA
ITALY
1
B-H YUG
BULG
6
SPAIN
9
5
ALB M
PORTUGAL
TURKEY

EST
LAT
LITH
SLO

MEXICO
1

ATLANTIC OCEAN

CUBA
DOMINICAN REPUBLIC
BELIZE JAMAICA
GUATEMALA HONDURAS HAITI
EL SALVADOR NICARAGUA
COSTA RICA PANAMA

ALGERIA
MOROCCO
WESTERN SAHARA

Armenia shut down its two nuclear plants after the 1988 earthquake, losing half its electricity capacity.

MAURITANIA
SENEGAL
GAMBIA MALI NIGER CHAD
GUINEA-BISSAU BURKINA FASO
GUINEA NIGERIA
SIERRA LEONE CÔTE d'IVOIRE GHANA BENIN
LIBERIA TOGO CAMEROON
EQUATORIAL GUINEA
SAO TOME & PRINCIPE GABON CONGO

PACIFIC OCEAN
VENEZUELA GUYANA
COLOMBIA SURINAME FRENCH GUIANA (Fr)
ECUADOR

BRAZIL
PERU
1

ANGOLA

NAMIBIA

NUCLEAR REACTORS NO LONGER IN SERVICE
1994
Source: *Nuclear News.*

BOLIVIA
PARAGUAY
CHILE

2
URUGUAY
ARGENTINA

FALKLAND ISLANDS (UK)

NUCLEAR DEPENDENCE
Percentage of electricity generated by nuclear power *1994*

50%
25%
10%
none

COMMERCIAL NUCLEAR POWER REACTORS *1994*

World total: 420 reactors

existing reactors
number given

UNSAFE REACTORS
in Eastern Europe and Russia according to International Atomic Energy Agency, 1993

very dangerous reactors

unsafe reactors

Sources: *Petroleum Economist;* U.S. Department of Energy; International Atomic Energy Agency; American Nuclear Society; *Bulletin of the Atomic Scientists;* UNEP; *Nuclear News;* press reports.

18
11
9 9
7
4
2 2 2
1 1

U.S. Russia France Germany UK Italy Armenia Canada Ukraine Spain Slovakia

Most states in the West are having second thoughts about nuclear power — but their atomic industries are searching out new markets in Asia and Eastern Europe.

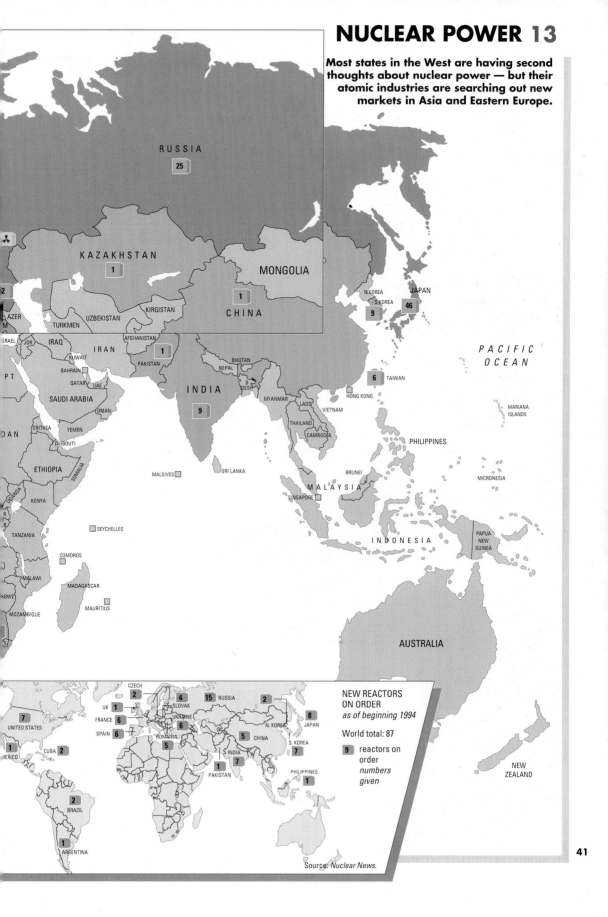

RUSSIA
25

KAZAKHSTAN
1

MONGOLIA

N.KOREA

S KOREA
9

JAPAN
46

AZER

UZBEKISTAN

KIRGISTAN

CHINA
1

TURKMEN

ISRAEL   JOR   IRAQ

IRAN

AFGHANISTAN
1

KUWAIT

PAKISTAN

BHUTAN

NEPAL

TAIWAN
6

PACIFIC
OCEAN

BAHRAIN

QATAR   UAE

INDIA

B DESH

HONG KONG

SAUDI ARABIA

OMAN

9

MYANMAR

LAOS

VIETNAM

MARIANA
ISLANDS

ERITREA   YEMEN

THAILAND

CAMBODIA

PHILIPPINES

DJIBOUTI

ETHIOPIA

SOMALIA

MALDIVES

SRI LANKA

BRUNEI

MICRONESIA

KENYA

MALAYSIA

SINGAPORE

TANZANIA

SEYCHELLES

COMOROS

INDONESIA

PAPUA
NEW
GUINEA

MALAWI

MADAGASCAR

MAURITIUS

BWE

MOZAMBIQUE

AUSTRALIA

**NEW REACTORS
ON ORDER**
as of beginning 1994

World total: 87

9 | reactors on
order
*numbers
given*

CZECH   2

UK   1

FRANCE   6

SPAIN   6

SLOVAK   4

UKRAINE   6

ROMANIA

5

RUSSIA   15

RUSSIA   2

N. KOREA   8

JAPAN

CHINA   5

S. KOREA   7

7

UNITED STATES   7

MEXICO   1

CUBA   2

INDIA   7

PAKISTAN   1

PHILIPPINES   1

NEW
ZEALAND

BRAZIL   2

ARGENTINA   1

Source: *Nuclear News.*

GREENLAND (DEN)

FAROE ISLANDS (DEN)

NORWAY   FINLAND

SWEDEN

Braer
1993

ESTONIA

LATVIA

DENMARK   LITHUANIA

Exxon
Valdez
1989

IRELAND

UNITED
KINGDOM

NETH

BEL   GERMANY

POLAND   BELAR

CZECH
REPUBLIC   UKRAIN

SLOVAK

C A N A D A

FRANCE   SWITZ   AUSTRIA   HUNGARY

SLO   CROATIA   ROMANI

B - H   YUG   BULGAR

ITALY   ALB   M

GREECE

Aegean
Sea
1992

U N I T E D   S T A T E S

O F   A M E R I C A

PORTUGAL   SPAIN

Juan Lavalleja
1980

Irenes Serenade 1980

Kharg 5 1989

MEXICO

Odyssey1988

TUNISIA

MOROCCO

ALGERIA   LIBYA

CUBA

DOMINICAN
REPUBLIC   WESTERN SAHARA

JAMAICA   PUERTO RICO (US)

BELIZE   HAITI

GUATEMALA   HONDURAS

EL SALVADOR

NICARAGUA

MAURITANIA   MALI   NIGER

A T L A N T I C

O C E A N

SENEGAL   BURKINA   CHAD

GAMBIA   FASO

GUINEA-BISSAU   GUINEA

COSTA RICA

PANAMA

VENEZUELA   GUYANA

SURINAME

FRENCH GUIANA (Fr)

SIERRA LEONE   CÔTE d'   NIGERIA   CAF

IVOIRE   GHANA   BENIN

LIBERIA   TOGO   CAMEROON

P A C I F I C

O C E A N

COLOMBIA

ECUADOR

EQUATORIAL GUINEA

GABON   Z A

CONGO

SOURCES OF MARINE OIL
POLLUTION early 1990s

atmospheric pollution
natural seeps
2% other
2% offshore production

ANGOLA

B R A Z I L

PERU   NAMIBIA

8%

10%

36%
urban and
industrial
runoff

BOLIVIA

PARAGUAY

12% tanker
accidents

CHILE

31%
regular shipping

SOU
AFRIC

Castillo de Belver
1983

URUGUAY

ARGENTINA

SUPPLY AND DEMAND FOR OIL
early 1990s

major oil consumers which
together account for 75%
of all oil consumption

other states

FALKLAND ISLANDS
(UK)

major oil producers states
which together account for
75% of all production

MARINE OIL POLLUTION

Source: Environmental
Almanac

FRONTIERS OF OIL EXPLORATION

1980s

oil spills from Persia
Gulf War 1992

oil rig blowout
1967 to early 1990s

1990s

major tanker spill
1980-93 over 35,000
metric tons spilled

Sources: OECD; Gaffney Cline; BP Statistical Review of World Energy; press reports

Modern industrial economies are dependent on oil, but allow trails of pollution to spread across the world's waterways.

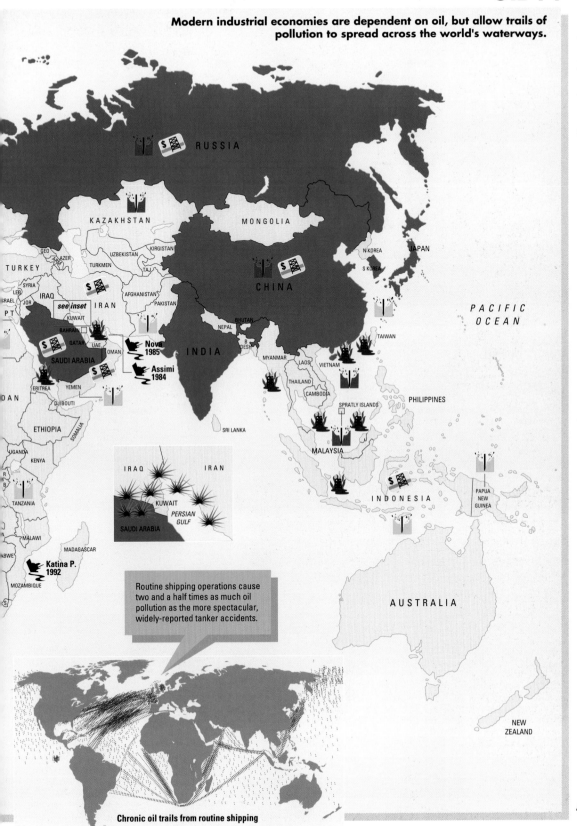

RUSSIA

KAZAKHSTAN

MONGOLIA

TURKEY

GEO
AZER
UZBEKISTAN
KIRGISTAN
TURKMEN
TAJ

SYRIA
LEB
IRAQ
ISRAEL
JOR
see inset
IRAN
AFGHANISTAN
PAKISTAN

KUWAIT
BAHRAIN
QATAR
UAE
OMAN

SAUDI ARABIA
YEMEN

ERITREA
DJIBOUTI

CHINA

N KOREA
S KOREA
JAPAN

TAIWAN

NEPAL
BHUTAN
B
DESH

INDIA

MYANMAR
LAOS
THAILAND
VIETNAM
CAMBODIA

PACIFIC
OCEAN

**Nova
1985**

**Assimi
1984**

SRI LANKA

SPRATLY ISLANDS

PHILIPPINES

MALAYSIA

ETHIOPIA

UGANDA
KENYA

TANZANIA

IRAQ   IRAN

KUWAIT
*PERSIAN
GULF*

SAUDI ARABIA

INDONESIA

PAPUA
NEW
GUINEA

MALAWI
MADAGASCAR

**Katina P.
1992**

MOZAMBIQUE

Routine shipping operations cause
two and a half times as much oil
pollution as the more spectacular,
widely-reported tanker accidents.

AUSTRALIA

NEW
ZEALAND

Chronic oil trails from routine shipping

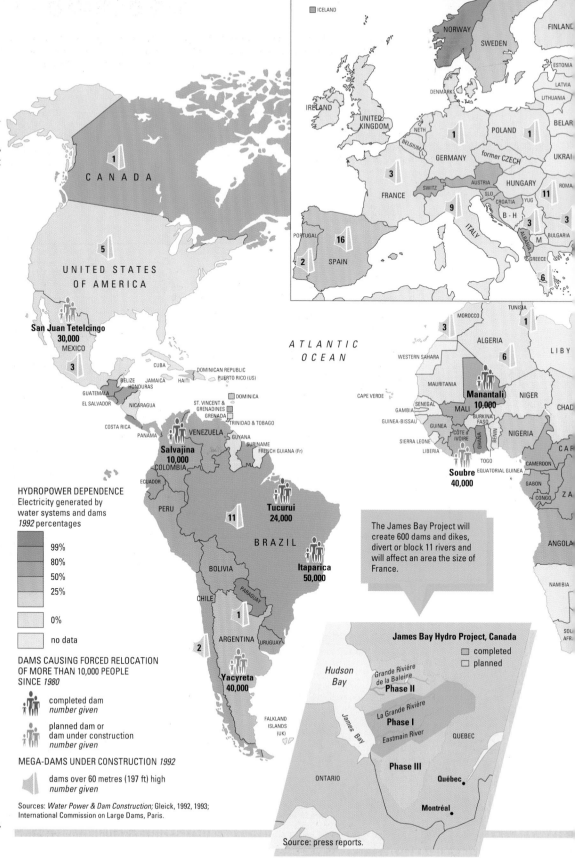

Copyright © Myriad Editions Limited

ICELAND

NORWAY   SWEDEN   FINLAND

IRELAND   DENMARK   ESTONIA   LATVIA   LITHUANIA

UNITED KINGDOM   NETH   BELGIUM   GERMANY   POLAND   BELAR   UKRAI

1   **1**

former CZECH   SWITZ   AUSTRIA   HUNGARY   ROMA

3   SLO   CROATIA   YUG   **11**

FRANCE

9   B - H   **3**   BULGARIA   **3**

PORTUGAL   **16**   SPAIN   ITALY   ALBANIA   M   GREECE

2   **6**

CANADA

1

UNITED STATES OF AMERICA

5

San Juan Tetelcingo
30,000
MEXICO

3

CUBA   DOMINICAN REPUBLIC   PUERTO RICO (US)
BELIZE   JAMAICA   HAITI
GUATEMALA   HONDURAS
EL SALVADOR   NICARAGUA
COSTA RICA
PANAMA   VENEZUELA   GUYANA

DOMINICA
ST. VINCENT & GRENADINES
GRENADA
TRINIDAD & TOBAGO
SURINAME
FRENCH GUIANA (Fr)

ATLANTIC OCEAN

Salvajina
10,000
COLOMBIA

ECUADOR

PERU

11

Tucurui
24,000

B R A Z I L

Itaparica
50,000

BOLIVIA

PARAGUAY

CHILE

1

2

ARGENTINA   URUGUAY

Yacyreta
40,000

FALKLAND ISLANDS (UK)

MOROCCO   TUNISIA   **1**

3   ALGERIA   LIBYA

WESTERN SAHARA   **6**

CAPE VERDE   MAURITANIA   MALI   NIGER   CHAD

Manantali
10,000

SENEGAL   GAMBIA   BURKINA FASO   NIGERIA
GUINEA-BISSAU   GUINEA   BENIN
SIERRA LEONE   CÔTE d'IVOIRE   GHANA
LIBERIA   TOGO   CAMEROON   CAR

Soubre
40,000

EQUATORIAL GUINEA   GABON   CONGO   ZA

ANGOLA

NAMIBIA

SOU AFR

The James Bay Project will create 600 dams and dikes, divert or block 11 rivers and will affect an area the size of France.

HYDROPOWER DEPENDENCE
Electricity generated by water systems and dams
1992 percentages

- 99%
- 80%
- 50%
- 25%
- 0%
- no data

DAMS CAUSING FORCED RELOCATION OF MORE THAN 10,000 PEOPLE SINCE *1980*

completed dam
number given

planned dam or dam under construction
number given

MEGA-DAMS UNDER CONSTRUCTION *1992*

dams over 60 metres (197 ft) high
number given

Sources: *Water Power & Dam Construction*; Gleick, 1992, 1993; International Commission on Large Dams, Paris.

James Bay Hydro Project, Canada

- completed
- planned

Hudson Bay

Grande Rivière de la Baleine
Phase II

La Grande Rivière
Phase I

James Bay

Eastmain River

QUEBEC

Phase III

ONTARIO

Québec ●

Montréal ●

Source: press reports.

Water can be a benign source of power for electricity, but engineering and economic imperatives often lead to giant dams that cause major hardship to people and nature.

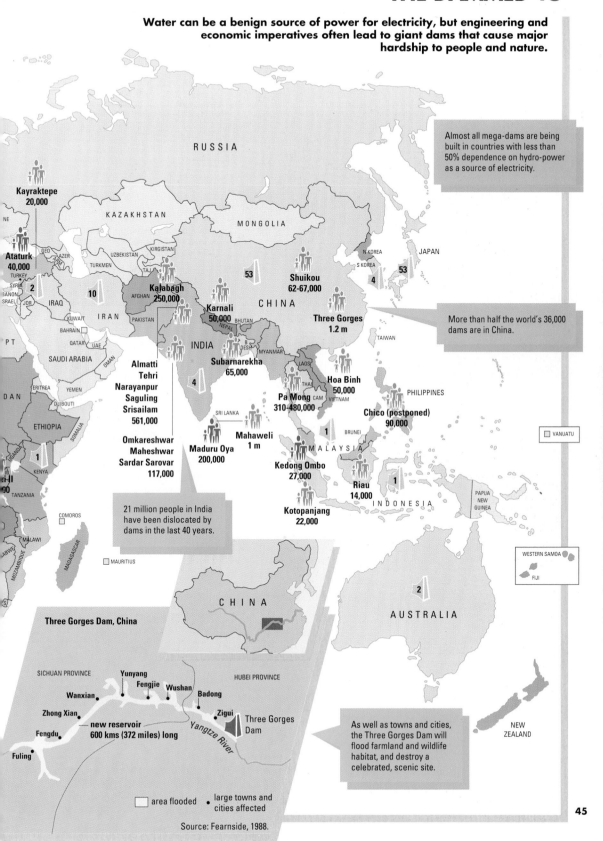

RUSSIA

KAZAKHSTAN

MONGOLIA

Almost all mega-dams are being built in countries with less than 50% dependence on hydro-power as a source of electricity.

Kayraktepe
20,000

NE

Ataturk
40,000

TURKEY
SYRIA
BANON
SRAEL
JOR
IRAQ
2
10
KUWAIT
BAHRAIN
QATAR   UAE
SAUDI ARABIA   OMAN
YEMEN
ERITREA
YEMEN
DJIBOUTI

GEO
AZER
UZBEKISTAN   KIRGISTAN
TURKMEN
TAJ
AFGHAN
IRAN
PAKISTAN

N KOREA   JAPAN
S KOREA
53
4   53

Shuikou
62-67,000

CHINA

Kalabagh
250,000

Karnali
50,000   BHUTAN
NEPAL

Three Gorges
1.2 m

TAIWAN

More than half the world's 36,000 dams are in China.

PT

DAN

ETHIOPIA

SOMALIA

Almatti
Tehri
Narayanpur
Saguling
Srisailam
561,000

Omkareshwar
Maheshwar
Sardar Sarovar
117,000

INDIA

B
DESH
MYANMAR
THAI
LAOS

Subarnarekha
65,000

4

Pa Mong
310-480,000

SRI LANKA

Maduru Oya
200,000

Mahaweli
1 m

Hoa Binh
50,000

CAM   VIETNAM

PHILIPPINES

Chico (postponed)
90,000

BRUNEI

1

MALAYSIA

Kedong Ombo
27,000

Kotopanjang
22,000

Riau
14,000

1

INDONESIA

PAPUA
NEW
GUINEA

VANUATU

UGANDA
1
KENYA
TANZANIA

COMOROS

MALAWI
ZIMBABWE
MOZAMBIQUE

MADAGASCAR

MAURITIUS

21 million people in India have been dislocated by dams in the last 40 years.

2

WESTERN SAMOA
FIJI

CHINA

AUSTRALIA

Three Gorges Dam, China

SICHUAN PROVINCE   Yunyang   HUBEI PROVINCE
Fengjie   Wushan
Wanxian   Badong
Zhong Xian   Zigui   Three Gorges
new reservoir   Dam
600 kms (372 miles) long   Yangtze River
Fengdu
Fuling

As well as towns and cities, the Three Gorges Dam will flood farmland and wildlife habitat, and destroy a celebrated, scenic site.

NEW
ZEALAND

☐ area flooded   • large towns and cities affected

Source: Fearnside, 1988.

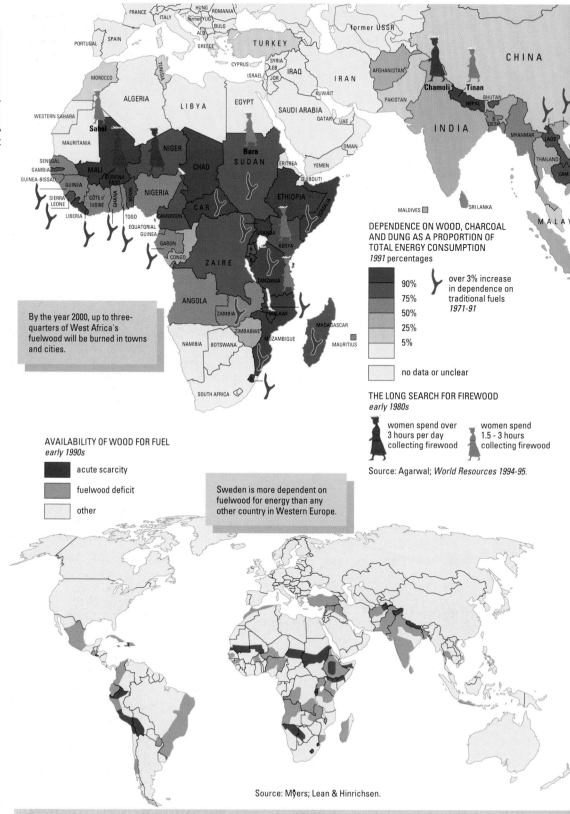

By the year 2000, up to three-quarters of West Africa's fuelwood will be burned in towns and cities.

DEPENDENCE ON WOOD, CHARCOAL AND DUNG AS A PROPORTION OF TOTAL ENERGY CONSUMPTION
1991 percentages

- 90%
- 75%
- 50%
- 25%
- 5%

over 3% increase in dependence on traditional fuels *1971-91*

no data or unclear

THE LONG SEARCH FOR FIREWOOD
early 1980s

women spend over 3 hours per day collecting firewood

women spend 1.5 - 3 hours collecting firewood

Source: Agarwal; *World Resources 1994-95.*

AVAILABILITY OF WOOD FOR FUEL
early 1990s

- acute scarcity
- fuelwood deficit
- other

Sweden is more dependent on fuelwood for energy than any other country in Western Europe.

Source: Myers; Lean & Hinrichsen.

Although firewood shortages are getting worse, dependence on traditional fuels is still increasing.

NUMBER OF PEOPLE FACING
ACUTE SCARCITY OF FIREWOOD
1980 and 2000 (projected) millions

	1980		2000

Source: FAO; Myers.

In Nepal, it takes 200-300 person-days per year to forage for a typical household's fuel.

1671m

East Asia

1024m

Latin America

512m

Africa, South of the Sahara

535m

Near East and North Africa

268m

227m

313m

104m

47

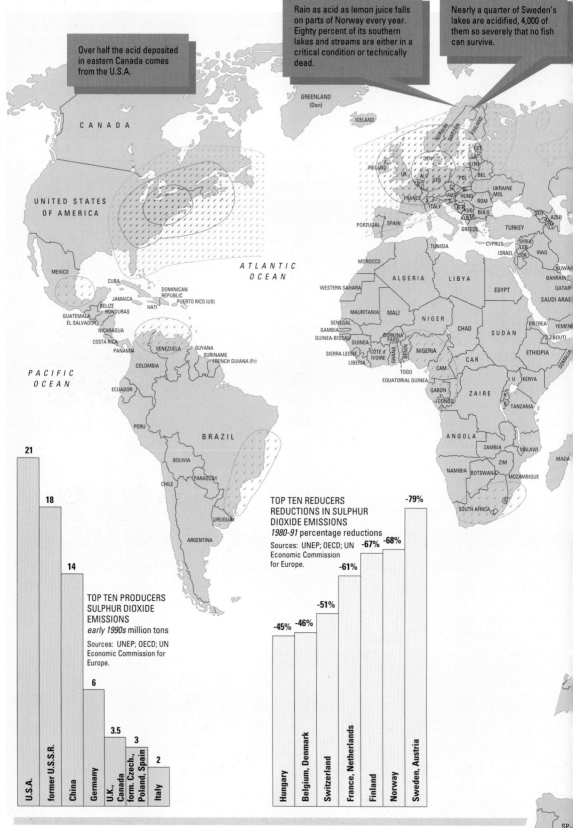

Over half the acid deposited in eastern Canada comes from the U.S.A.

Rain as acid as lemon juice falls on parts of Norway every year. Eighty percent of its southern lakes and streams are either in a critical condition or technically dead.

Nearly a quarter of Sweden's lakes are acidified, 4,000 of them so severely that no fish can survive.

TOP TEN PRODUCERS
SULPHUR DIOXIDE
EMISSIONS
early 1990s million tons

Sources: UNEP; OECD; UN Economic Commission for Europe.

- U.S.A. — 21
- former U.S.S.R. — 18
- China — 14
- Germany — 6
- U.K., Canada — 3.5
- form. Czech., Poland, Spain — 3
- Italy — 2

TOP TEN REDUCERS
REDUCTIONS IN SULPHUR DIOXIDE EMISSIONS
1980-91 percentage reductions

Sources: UNEP; OECD; UN Economic Commission for Europe.

- Hungary — -45%
- Belgium, Denmark — -46%
- Switzerland — -51%
- France, Netherlands — -61%
- Finland — -67%
- Norway — -68%
- Sweden, Austria — -79%

Acid rain attacks lakes, rivers, forests and buildings. It ignores state boundaries and its source often lies abroad.

RUSSIA
KAZAKHSTAN
MONGOLIA
KIRG
TAJ
AFGHAN
CHINA
N KOREA
S.KOREA
JAPAN
PAKISTAN
NEPAL
BHUTAN
B DESH
INDIA
MYANMAR
LAOS
THAI
VIETNAM
CAM
TAIWAN
HONG KONG
PHILIPPINES
SRI LANKA
BRUNEI
MALAYSIA
INDONESIA
PAPUA NEW GUINEA
AUSTRALIA
NEW ZEALAND

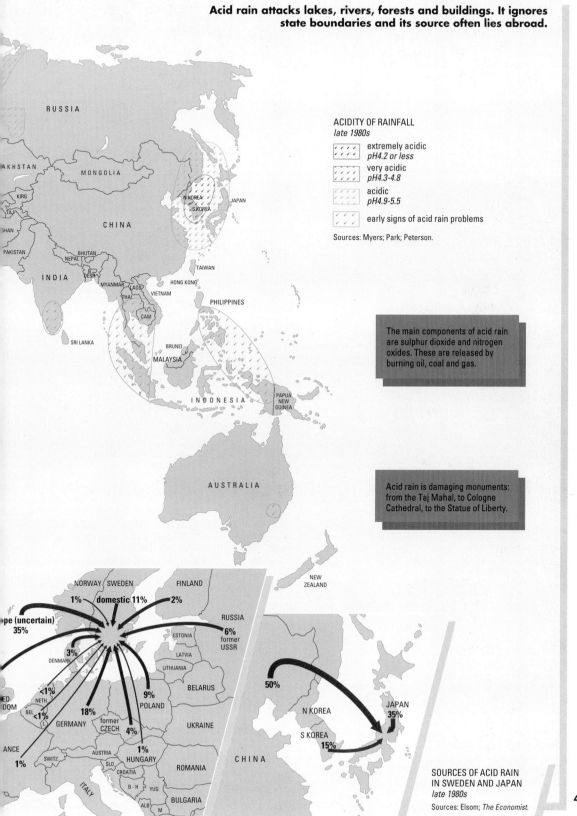

ACIDITY OF RAINFALL
late 1980s

- extremely acidic *pH4.2 or less*
- very acidic *pH4.3-4.8*
- acidic *pH4.9-5.5*
- early signs of acid rain problems

Sources: Myers; Park; Peterson.

The main components of acid rain are sulphur dioxide and nitrogen oxides. These are released by burning oil, coal and gas.

Acid rain is damaging monuments: from the Taj Mahal, to Cologne Cathedral, to the Statue of Liberty.

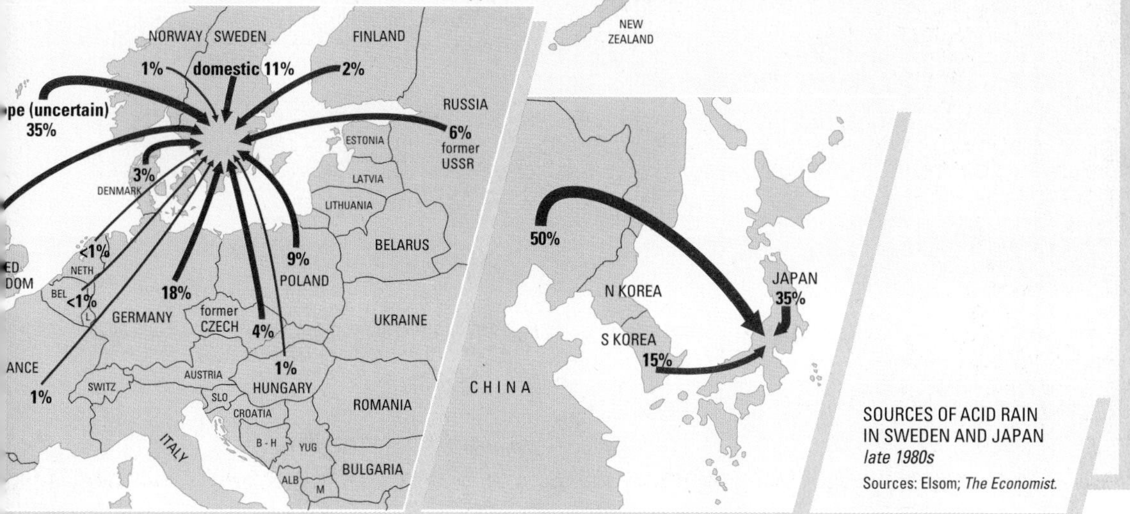
NORWAY
SWEDEN
FINLAND
1%
domestic 11%
2%
pe (uncertain) 35%
RUSSIA
6% former USSR
ESTONIA
LATVIA
LITHUANIA
3%
DENMARK
BELARUS
<1%
NETH
BEL
<1%
ED DOM
18%
9%
POLAND
GERMANY
former CZECH
4%
UKRAINE
ANCE
1%
1%
AUSTRIA
SWITZ
HUNGARY
SLO
CROATIA
ROMANIA
ITALY
B-H
YUG
ALB
M
BULGARIA
50%
N KOREA
S KOREA
15%
JAPAN
35%
CHINA

SOURCES OF ACID RAIN IN SWEDEN AND JAPAN
late 1980s

Sources: Elsom; *The Economist.*

The Intergovernmental Panel on Climate Change, convened by the UN, concluded in 1990 that human activities are already altering the atmosphere. But some scientists still doubt the existence of global warming.

GREENLAND (Den)

ICELAND

C A N A D A

NORWAY   SWEDEN

IRELAND   UK   DENMARK

UNITED STATES OF AMERICA

NETH.
BEL   GERMANY   POLAN
former CZ
FRANCE   AUS   HUN
S   former
ITALY

PORTUGAL   SPAIN   GRE

Harvests in the American Midwest could be cut by up to a third.

MEXICO

BAHAMAS

CUBA
DOMINICAN
REPUBLIC
PUERTO RICO (US)

BELIZE   JAMAICA
HONDURAS   HAITI

GUATEMALA
EL SALVADOR
NICARAGUA
COSTA RICA

ATLANTIC
OCEAN

MOROCCO   TUNISIA

ALGERIA   LIBY

WESTERN SAHARA

CAPE VERDE
ISLANDS

MAURITANIA   MALI   NIGER   CHA

SENEGAL
GAMBIA
GUINEA-BISSAU   GUINEA   BURKINA
FASO   NIGERIA
SIERRA   CÔTE d'   GHANA
LEONE   IVOIRE   BENIN
LIBERIA   TOGO
EQUATORIAL   CAMEROON   C
GUINEA   GABON
CON   Z

Heat stress could threaten cloud forest in Costa Rica.

PANAMA

VENEZUELA
GUYANA
SURINAME
FRENCH GUIANA (Fr)

COLOMBIA

ECUADOR

Rising sea levels would flood breeding beaches of turtles, marine iguanas, and sea lions on the Galapagos Islands.

PERU

B R A Z I L

ANGOL

BOLIVIA

NAMIBIA

GREENHOUSE GASES
Proportion of global warming attributed to various gases *1992*

CHILE   PARAGUAY

ARGENTINA   URUGUAY

GREENHOUSE GAS PRODUCERS
Shares of world output *1989* percentages

	10%
	5%
	2.5%
	1%
	0.5%
	0.1
	other

nitrous oxide
6%

carbon dioxide
55%

FALKLAND ISLANDS
(UK)

areas vulnerable to flooding if sea level rises

biosphere reserve threatened by global warming *early 1990s*

methane
15%   CFCs
24%

Biosphere reserves are places identified by UNESCO as sites of exceptionally rich or unique plant and animal communities.

Sources: Intergovernmental Panel on Climate Change (IPCC); Myers; World Wide Fund for Nature (WWF); Marshall, ed.

Source: U.S. Office of Technology Assessment

Scan

Global warming will wreak havoc with the world's ecosystems. Even conservative predictions point to the likelihood of sea level rises, increases in storm intensity, and disruptions in food production.

The tundra ecosystems of Siberia and Canada would be disrupted by rising temperatures and by vegetation belts shifting northward.

former USSR

MONGOLIA

N KOREA

S KOREA

JAPAN

Up to 18% of Bangladesh could be under water by 2050.

TURKEY

SYRIA
LEB
ISRAEL
JOR
IRAQ

IRAN

AFGHANISTAN

PAKISTAN

CHINA

PACIFIC
OCEAN

KUWAIT
BAHRAIN
QATAR
UAE

EPT

QP T

SAUDI ARABIA

OMAN

BHUTAN

NEPAL

INDIA

TAIWAN

MYANMAR

LAOS

VIETNAM

THAI

CAM

MARIANA
ISLANDS

PHILIPPINES

ERITREA

YEMEN

DAN

DJIBOUTI

SOMALIA

ETHIOPIA

MALDIVES

SRI LANKA

BRUNEI

MICRONESIA

UGANDA

KENYA

MALAYSIA

R
B

TANZANIA

INDONESIA

PAPUA
NEW
GUINEA

MALAWI

MAURITIUS

ABWE

MOZAMBIQUE

MADAGASCAR

Intro (beginning)

AUSTRALIA

NEW
ZEALAND

Cyclones are likely to become more frequent and more severe as a result of global warming.

STORM WARMING

tropical cyclone belts

38% Finland

 44% Denmark, Norway
47% Switzerland
48% Japan

 51% Hungary
54% Poland
56% U.S.A.

 65% Netherlands
66% Portugal
67% Philippines, UK
68% Canada, Ireland
69% India

 71% Mexico
73% Chile
74% Germany
76% Nigeria, S. Korea

 81% Brazil
83% Uruguay
85% Russia

SHARE OF POPULATION
WHICH STRONGLY FAVORS
STRONGER ENVIRONMENTAL LAWS
FOR BUSINESS AND INDUSTRY
1992

Source: Gallup International Institute 1992

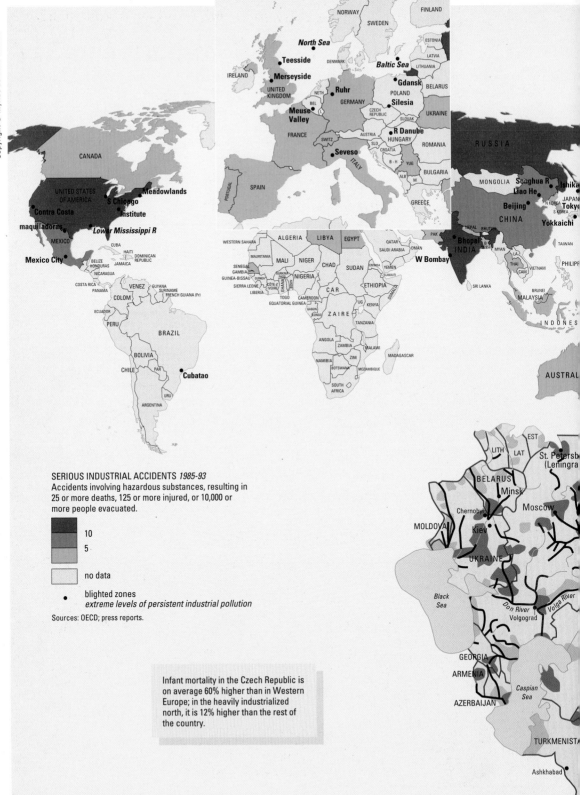

CANADA

UNITED STATES
OF AMERICA

Meadowlands
S Chicago
Institute
Contra Costa
Lower Mississippi R
maquiladoras
MEXICO
Mexico City

CUBA
HAITI
BELIZE
HONDURAS
JAMAICA
DOMINICAN
REPUBLIC
NICARAGUA
GUATEMALA
COSTA RICA
PANAMA

VENEZ
GUYANA
SURINAME
FRENCH GUIANA (Fr)
COLOM
ECUADOR
PERU
BRAZIL
BOLIVIA
CHILE
PAR
URU
ARGENTINA

Cubatao

NORWAY
SWEDEN
FINLAND
North Sea
Teesside
DENMARK
ESTONIA
LATVIA
LITHUANIA
Baltic Sea
IRELAND
Merseyside
UNITED
KINGDOM
NETH
BEL
Ruhr
Gdansk
POLAND
BELARUS
GERMANY
Silesia
Meuse
Valley
CZECH
REPUBLIC
UKRAINE
FRANCE
SWITZ
AUSTRIA
SLOVAK
SLO
HUNGARY
R Danube
ROMANIA
CROATIA
Seveso
B - H
YUG
ITALY
ALB
M
BULGARIA
SPAIN
PORTUGAL
GREECE

WESTERN SAHARA
ALGERIA
LIBYA
EGYPT
QATAR
OMAN
SAUDI ARABIA
MAURITANIA
MALI
NIGER
CHAD
SUDAN
ERITREA
YEMEN
SENEGAL
GAMBIA
BURKINA
GUINEA
DJIBOUTI
GUINEA-BISSAU
SIERRA LEONE
CÔTE
D'IVOIRE
GHANA
NIGERIA
BENIN
TOGO
CAMEROON
CAR
ETHIOPIA
SOMALIA
LIBERIA
EQUATORIAL GUINEA
GABON
CONGO
UG
KENYA
ZAIRE
TANZANIA
ANGOLA
ZAMBIA
MALAWI
MADAGASCAR
NAMIBIA
ZIM
MOZAMBIQUE
BOTSWANA
SOUTH
AFRICA

RUSSIA
MONGOLIA
Songhua R
Ishika
Liao He
JAPAN
N KOREA
Tokyo
Beijing
S KOREA
CHINA
Yokkaichi
NEPAL
BHUTAN
Bhopal
INDIA
MYAN
W Bombay
LA
THAI
CAM
VIETNAM
PHILIPP
SRI LANKA
BRUNEI
MALAYSIA
INDONES
PAK
TAIWAN
AUSTRAL

SERIOUS INDUSTRIAL ACCIDENTS 1985-93
Accidents involving hazardous substances, resulting in
25 or more deaths, 125 or more injured, or 10,000 or
more people evacuated.

- 10
- 5
- no data
- • blighted zones
  extreme levels of persistent industrial pollution

Sources: OECD; press reports.

Infant mortality in the Czech Republic is
on average 60% higher than in Western
Europe; in the heavily industrialized
north, it is 12% higher than the rest of
the country.

EST
LITH
LAT
St. Petersb
(Leningra
BELARUS
Minsk
Chernobyl
Moscow
MOLDOVA
Kiev
UKRAINE
Black
Sea
Don River
Volga River
Volgograd
GEORGIA
ARMENIA
Caspian
Sea
AZERBAIJAN
TURKMENISTA
Ashkhabad

Much of the former USSR is in a state of ecological crisis.

ENVIRONMENTAL DEGRADATION IN RUSSIA AND
OTHER STATES OF THE FORMER USSR
1993

- castastrophic degradation
  irreparable pollution and degradation
- critical degradation
  serious threat to human health
- stretches of heavily polluted river

Source: Peterson; Russian Academy of Sciences.

NEW
ZEALAND

Murmansk

Forty percent of industrial
workers in the Murmansk region
suffer from respiratory disease.

Arkhangelsk

Kolyma River

Lena River

Norilsk

R U S S I A

Nizhnii Novgorod
(Gorkii)

Pechora River

Ob River

Yenisei River

Yekaterinburg
(Sverdlovsk)

Komsomolsk-
on-Amur

Chelyabinsk

Amur River

Omsk

Krasnoyarsk

Bratsk

Novosibirsk

Kemerovo

Lake
Baikal

KAZAKHSTAN

Irkutsk

Vladivostok

Semipalatinsk

Lake Balkhash

A quarter of the population of the
former USSR live in regions of critical
or castastrophic degradation.

Syrdarya

UZBEKISTAN

Alma Ata

Bishkek
KIRGISTAN

TAJIKISTAN

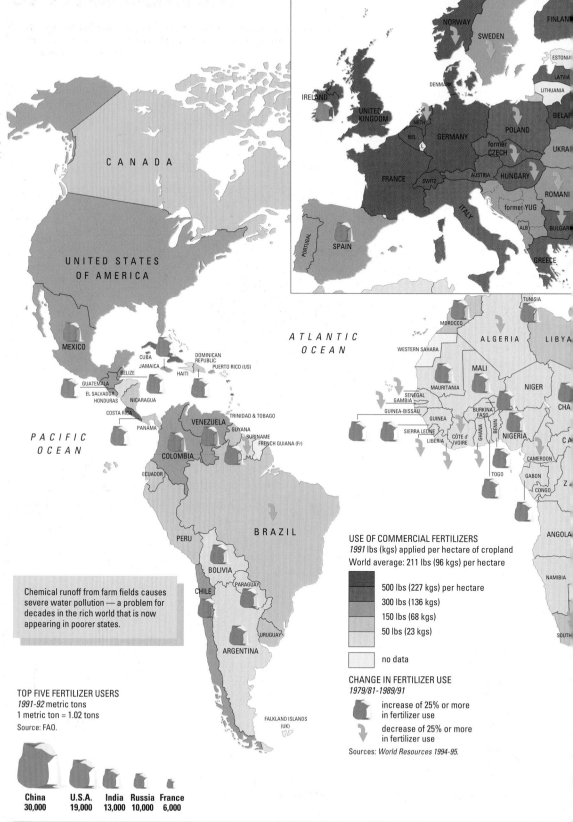

Copyright © Myriad Editions Limited

CANADA

UNITED STATES
OF AMERICA

MEXICO

GUATEMALA
EL SALVADOR
HONDURAS
COSTA RICA
NICARAGUA

CUBA
JAMAICA
BELIZE
HAITI
DOMINICAN
REPUBLIC
PUERTO RICO (US)

PANAMA

PACIFIC
OCEAN

VENEZUELA
GUYANA
TRINIDAD & TOBAGO
SURINAME
FRENCH GUIANA (Fr)

COLOMBIA
ECUADOR

PERU

BRAZIL

BOLIVIA
PARAGUAY
CHILE

URUGUAY
ARGENTINA

FALKLAND ISLANDS
(UK)

ATLANTIC
OCEAN

NORWAY
SWEDEN
FINLAND

IRELAND
UNITED
KINGDOM
DENMARK
ESTONIA
LATVIA
LITHUANIA
NETH
BEL
GERMANY
POLAND
former
CZECH
BELAR
UKRA
FRANCE
SWITZ
AUSTRIA
HUNGARY
ROMANI
ITALY
former YUG
ALB
BULGAR
PORTUGAL
SPAIN
GREECE

TUNISIA
MOROCCO
WESTERN SAHARA
ALGERIA
LIBYA
MALI
NIGER
CHA
MAURITANIA
SENEGAL
GAMBIA
GUINEA-BISSAU
GUINEA
BURKINA
FASO
BENIN
NIGERIA
SIERRA LEONE
GHANA
CÔTE d'
IVOIRE
LIBERIA
CAMEROON
TOGO
GABON
CONGO
Z
CA
ANGOLA
NAMIBIA
SOUTH

Chemical runoff from farm fields causes
severe water pollution — a problem for
decades in the rich world that is now
appearing in poorer states.

USE OF COMMERCIAL FERTILIZERS
1991 lbs (kgs) applied per hectare of cropland
World average: 211 lbs (96 kgs) per hectare

500 lbs (227 kgs) per hectare
300 lbs (136 kgs)
150 lbs (68 kgs)
50 lbs (23 kgs)

no data

CHANGE IN FERTILIZER USE
1979/81-1989/91

increase of 25% or more
in fertilizer use

decrease of 25% or more
in fertilizer use

Sources: *World Resources 1994-95.*

TOP FIVE FERTILIZER USERS
1991-92 metric tons
1 metric ton = 1.02 tons
Source: FAO.

China	U.S.A.	India	Russia	France
30,000	19,000	13,000	10,000	6,000

THE FARMING FIX 20

Heavy use of commercial fertilizers disrupts soil balance and crop ecology — and creates an ever-increasing cycle of fertilizer dependence.

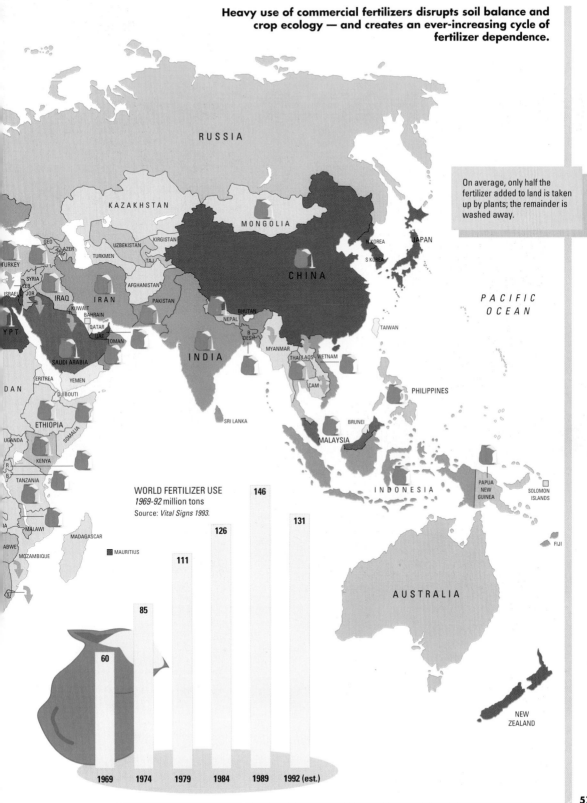

On average, only half the fertilizer added to land is taken up by plants; the remainder is washed away.

WORLD FERTILIZER USE
1969-92 million tons
Source: *Vital Signs 1993.*

■ MAURITIUS

1969	1974	1979	1984	1989	1992 (est.)
60	85	111	126	146	131

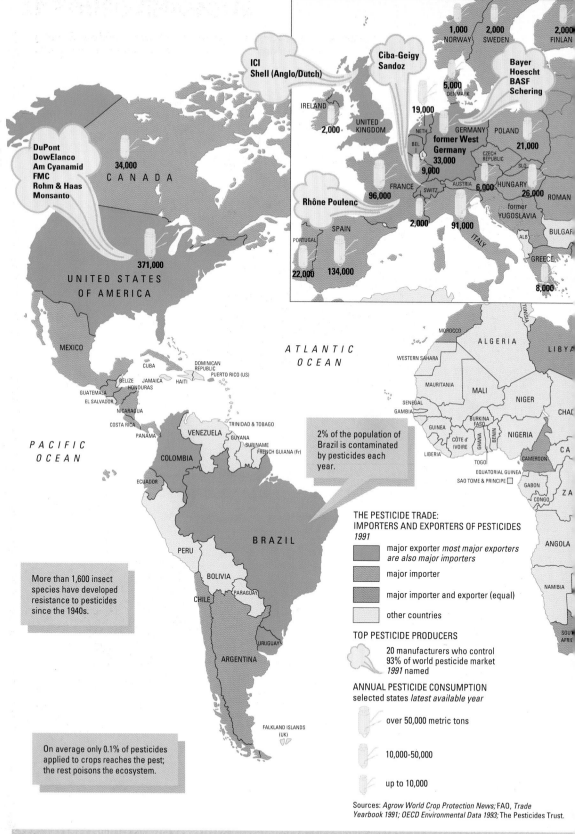

DuPont
DowElanco
Am Cyanamid
FMC
Rohm & Haas
Monsanto

C A N A D A

34,000

371,000

UNITED STATES
OF AMERICA

ICI
Shell (Anglo/Dutch)

Ciba-Geigy
Sandoz

Bayer
Hoescht
BASF
Schering

1,000
NORWAY

2,000
SWEDEN

2,000
FINLAN

5,000
DENMARK

IRELAND

19,000

2,000

UNITED
KINGDOM

NETH

former West
Germany
33,000

GERMANY

POLAND

21,000

BEL

9,000

FRANCE

96,000

SWITZ

CZECH
REPUBLIC

SLO

AUSTRIA

6,000

HUNGARY

26,000

ROMAN

Rhône Poulenc

2,000

91,000

former
YUGOSLAVIA

ITALY

ALB

BULGAR

SPAIN

PORTUGAL

22,000

134,000

GREECE

8,000

A T L A N T I C
O C E A N

MEXICO

CUBA

DOMINICAN
REPUBLIC

PUERTO RICO (US)

BELIZE   JAMAICA   HAITI
GUATEMALA   HONDURAS
EL SALVADOR
NICARAGUA

COSTA RICA

PANAMA

TRINIDAD & TOBAGO

VENEZUELA   GUYANA
SURINAME
FRENCH GUIANA (Fr)

COLOMBIA

ECUADOR

P A C I F I C
O C E A N

MOROCCO

ALGERIA

LIBYA

WESTERN SAHARA

MAURITANIA

MALI

NIGER

CHAD

SENEGAL
GAMBIA

GUINEA

BURKINA
FASO

NIGERIA

CÔTE d'
IVOIRE

GHANA

BENIN

LIBERIA

TOGO

CAMEROON

C A

EQUATORIAL GUINEA
SAO TOME & PRINCIPE

GABON

Z A

CONGO

2% of the population of
Brazil is contaminated
by pesticides each
year.

PERU

B R A Z I L

ANGOLA

BOLIVIA

More than 1,600 insect
species have developed
resistance to pesticides
since the 1940s.

PARAGUAY

NAMIBIA

CHILE

URUGUAY

ARGENTINA

SOU
AFRIC

FALKLAND ISLANDS
(UK)

On average only 0.1% of pesticides
applied to crops reaches the pest;
the rest poisons the ecosystem.

THE PESTICIDE TRADE:
IMPORTERS AND EXPORTERS OF PESTICIDES
1991

major exporter *most major exporters
are also major importers*

major importer

major importer and exporter (equal)

other countries

TOP PESTICIDE PRODUCERS

20 manufacturers who control
93% of world pesticide market
1991 named

ANNUAL PESTICIDE CONSUMPTION
selected states *latest available year*

over 50,000 metric tons

10,000-50,000

up to 10,000

Sources: *Agrow World Crop Protection News;* FAO, *Trade
Yearbook 1991;* OECD *Environmental Data 1993;* The Pesticides Trust.

Pesticides frequently fail to protect plant crops, while poisoning land, animals and people.

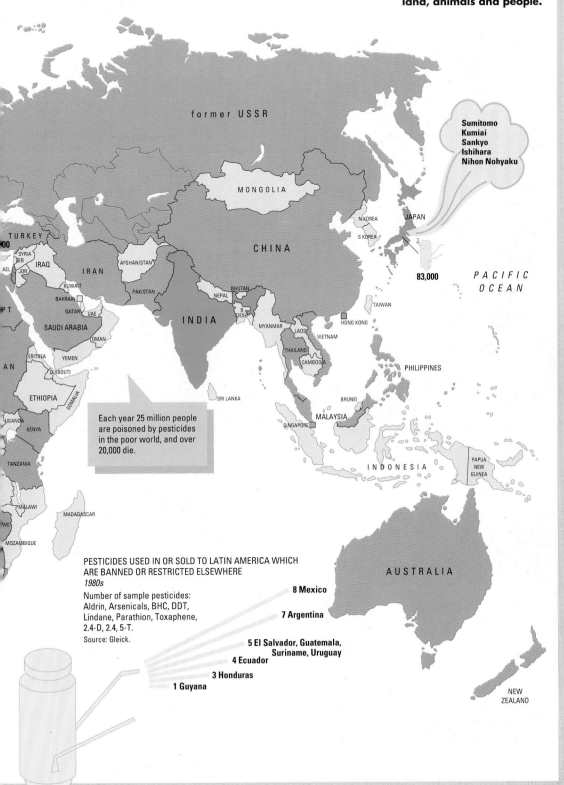

former USSR

MONGOLIA

Sumitomo
Kumiai
Sankyo
Ishihara
Nihon Nohyaku

N KOREA

JAPAN

S KOREA

CHINA

83,000

PACIFIC
OCEAN

TURKEY

00

SYRIA
DEB
AEL JOR
IRAQ

IRAN

AFGHANISTAN

KUWAIT

BAHRAIN

PT

QATAR UAE

SAUDI ARABIA

OMAN

PAKISTAN

NEPAL

BHUTAN

B
DESH

INDIA

MYANMAR

LAOS

VIETNAM

THAILAND

CAMBODIA

TAIWAN

HONG KONG

PHILIPPINES

ERITREA YEMEN

A N

DJIBOUTI

ETHIOPIA

SOMALIA

UGANDA

KENYA

SRI LANKA

BRUNEI

MALAYSIA

SINGAPORE

Each year 25 million people
are poisoned by pesticides
in the poor world, and over
20,000 die.

TANZANIA

MALAWI

MADAGASCAR

WE

MOZAMBIQUE

INDONESIA

PAPUA
NEW
GUINEA

AUSTRALIA

PESTICIDES USED IN OR SOLD TO LATIN AMERICA WHICH
ARE BANNED OR RESTRICTED ELSEWHERE
1980s
Number of sample pesticides:
Aldrin, Arsenicals, BHC, DDT,
Lindane, Parathion, Toxaphene,
2.4-D, 2.4, 5-T.
Source: Gleick.

8 Mexico

7 Argentina

5 El Salvador, Guatemala,
Suriname, Uruguay
4 Ecuador

3 Honduras

1 Guyana

NEW
ZEALAND

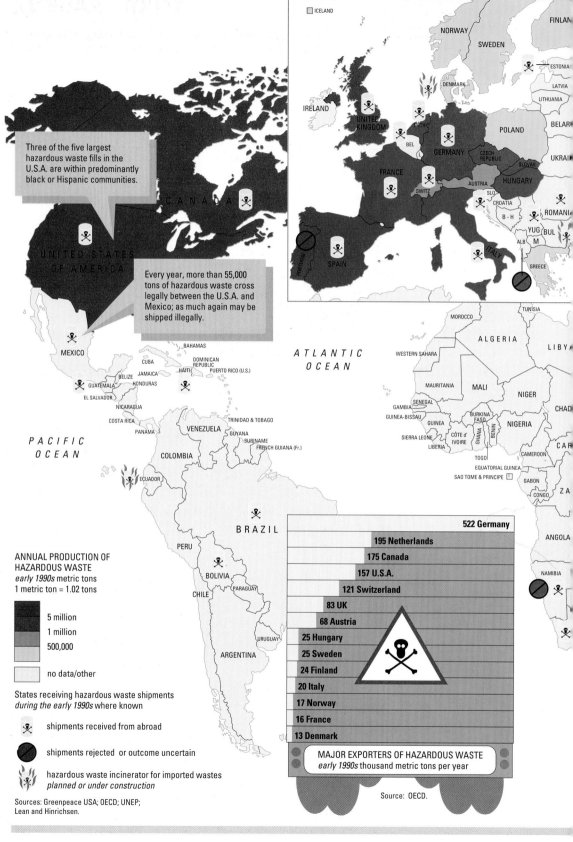

Three of the five largest hazardous waste fills in the U.S.A. are within predominantly black or Hispanic communities.

Every year, more than 55,000 tons of hazardous waste cross legally between the U.S.A. and Mexico; as much again may be shipped illegally.

ANNUAL PRODUCTION OF HAZARDOUS WASTE
early 1990s metric tons
1 metric ton = 1.02 tons

- 5 million
- 1 million
- 500,000
- no data/other

States receiving hazardous waste shipments *during the early 1990s* where known

- shipments received from abroad
- shipments rejected or outcome uncertain
- hazardous waste incinerator for imported wastes *planned or under construction*

Sources: Greenpeace USA; OECD; UNEP; Lean and Hinrichsen.

MAJOR EXPORTERS OF HAZARDOUS WASTE
early 1990s thousand metric tons per year

- 522 Germany
- 195 Netherlands
- 175 Canada
- 157 U.S.A.
- 121 Switzerland
- 83 UK
- 68 Austria
- 25 Hungary
- 25 Sweden
- 24 Finland
- 20 Italy
- 17 Norway
- 16 France
- 13 Denmark

Source: OECD.

ATLANTIC OCEAN

PACIFIC OCEAN

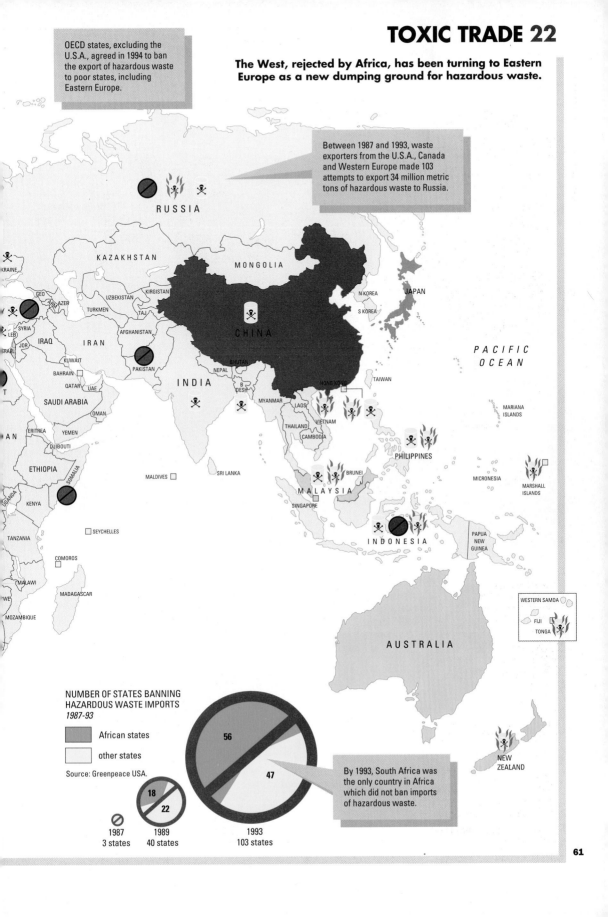

OECD states, excluding the U.S.A., agreed in 1994 to ban the export of hazardous waste to poor states, including Eastern Europe.

The West, rejected by Africa, has been turning to Eastern Europe as a new dumping ground for hazardous waste.

Between 1987 and 1993, waste exporters from the U.S.A., Canada and Western Europe made 103 attempts to export 34 million metric tons of hazardous waste to Russia.

RUSSIA

KAZAKHSTAN

MONGOLIA

N KOREA

JAPAN

S KOREA

KRAINE

GEO

AZER

ARM

UZBEKISTAN

KIRGISTAN

SYRIA

TURKMEN

TAJ.

LEB

IRAQ

IRAN

AFGHANISTAN

CHINA

RAEL

JOR

KUWAIT

PAKISTAN

BAHRAIN

NEPAL

BHUTAN

QATAR

UAE

INDIA

B DESH

TAIWAN

HONG KONG

SAUDI ARABIA

OMAN

MYANMAR

LAOS

PACIFIC OCEAN

AN

ERITREA

YEMEN

THAILAND

VIETNAM

CAMBODIA

DJIBOUTI

MARIANA ISLANDS

ETHIOPIA

SOMALIA

MALDIVES

SRI LANKA

PHILIPPINES

UGANDA

KENYA

MICRONESIA

MARSHALL ISLANDS

BRUNEI

MALAYSIA

TANZANIA

SEYCHELLES

SINGAPORE

COMOROS

INDONESIA

PAPUA NEW GUINEA

MALAWI

MADAGASCAR

WE

MOZAMBIQUE

AUSTRALIA

WESTERN SAMOA

FIJI

TONGA

NUMBER OF STATES BANNING HAZARDOUS WASTE IMPORTS
1987-93

African states

other states

Source: Greenpeace USA.

56

47

18

22

NEW ZEALAND

By 1993, South Africa was the only country in Africa which did not ban imports of hazardous waste.

1987
3 states

1989
40 states

1993
103 states

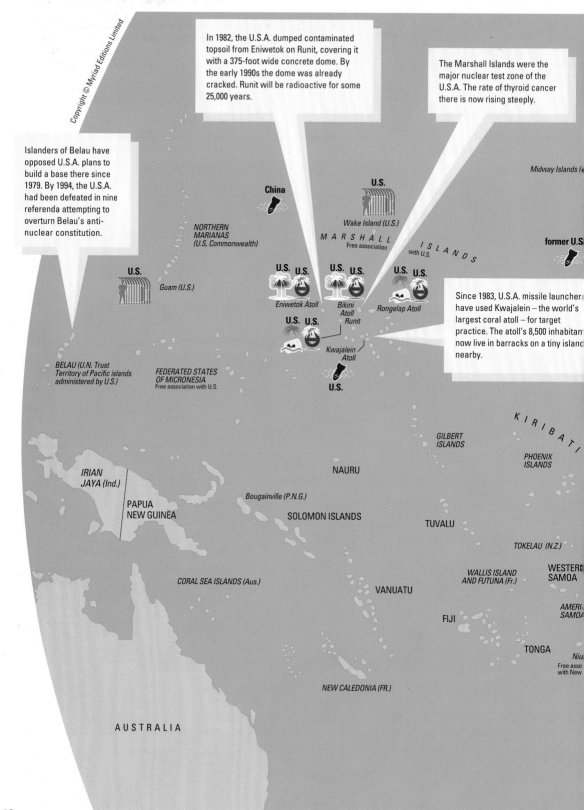

In 1982, the U.S.A. dumped contaminated topsoil from Eniwetok on Runit, covering it with a 375-foot wide concrete dome. By the early 1990s the dome was already cracked. Runit will be radioactive for some 25,000 years.

The Marshall Islands were the major nuclear test zone of the U.S.A. The rate of thyroid cancer there is now rising steeply.

Islanders of Belau have opposed U.S.A. plans to build a base there since 1979. By 1994, the U.S.A. had been defeated in nine referenda attempting to overturn Belau's anti-nuclear constitution.

Since 1983, U.S.A. missile launcher have used Kwajalein – the world's largest coral atoll – for target practice. The atoll's 8,500 inhabitant now live in barracks on a tiny island nearby.

China

U.S.

Midway Islands (

Wake Island (U.S.)

NORTHERN
MARIANAS
(U.S, Commonwealth)

M A R S H A L L
Free association
with U.S.

I S L A N D S

former U.S

U.S. U.S.

U.S. U.S.

U.S. U.S.

Guam (U.S.)

Eniwetok Atoll

Bikini
Atoll
Runit

Rongelap Atoll

U.S. U.S.

Kwajalein
Atoll

BELAU (U.N. Trust
Territory of Pacific islands
administered by U.S.)

FEDERATED STATES
OF MICRONESIA
Free association with U.S.

U.S.

K I R I B A T I

GILBERT
ISLANDS

PHOENIX
ISLANDS

IRIAN
JAYA (Ind.)

PAPUA
NEW GUINEA

NAURU

Bougainville (P.N.G.)

SOLOMON ISLANDS

TUVALU

TOKELAU (N.Z.)

CORAL SEA ISLANDS (Aus.)

VANUATU

WALLIS ISLAND
AND FUTUNA (Fr.)

WESTERN
SAMOA

AMERI
SAMOA

FIJI

TONGA

Niu
Free asso
with New

NEW CALEDONIA (FR.)

AUSTRALIA

The South Pacific is many people's idea of paradise. But nuclear testing has made some formerly idyllic islands radioactive for thousands of years and turned their inhabitants into refugees.

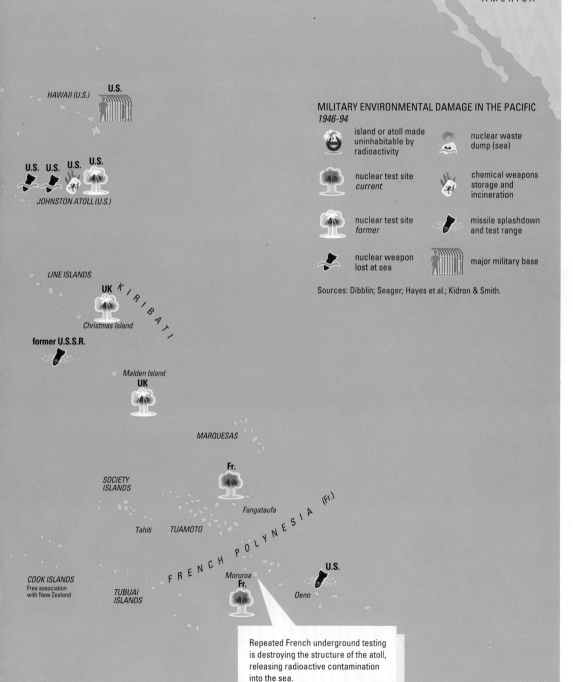

NORTH
AMERICA

HAWAII (U.S.)   U.S.

U.S.   U.S.   U.S.   U.S.

JOHNSTON ATOLL (U.S.)

LINE ISLANDS

UK   K I R I B A T I

Christmas Island

former U.S.S.R.

Malden Island
UK

MARQUESAS

Fr.

SOCIETY
ISLANDS

Fangataufa

Tahiti   TUAMOTO

F R E N C H   P O L Y N E S I A (Fr.)

COOK ISLANDS
Free association
with New Zealand

TUBUAI
ISLANDS

Moruroa
Fr.

U.S.

Oeno

Repeated French underground testing
is destroying the structure of the atoll,
releasing radioactive contamination
into the sea.

MILITARY ENVIRONMENTAL DAMAGE IN THE PACIFIC
1946-94

island or atoll made uninhabitable by radioactivity

nuclear waste dump (sea)

nuclear test site *current*

chemical weapons storage and incineration

nuclear test site *former*

missile splashdown and test range

nuclear weapon lost at sea

major military base

Sources: Dibblin; Seager; Hayes et al.; Kidron & Smith.

When war breaks out, the environment is always a casualty.

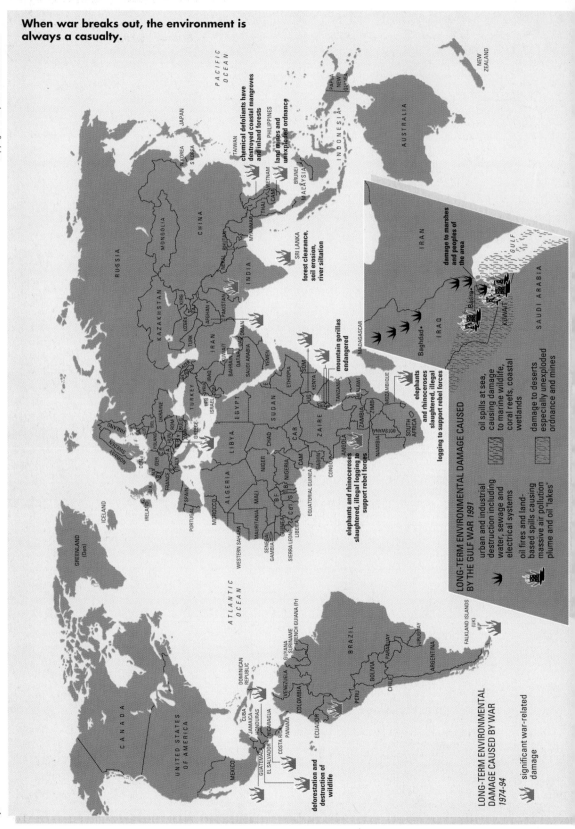

chemical defoliants have destroyed coastal mangroves and inland forests

land mines and unexploded ordnance

forest clearance, soil erosion, river siltation

mountain gorillas endangered

damage to marshes and peoples of the area

elephants and rhinoceroses slaughtered, illegal logging to support rebel forces

elephants and rhinoceroses slaughtered, illegal logging to support rebel forces

deforestation and destruction of wildlife

LONG-TERM ENVIRONMENTAL DAMAGE CAUSED BY THE GULF WAR *1991*

urban and industrial destruction including water, sewage and electrical systems

oil fires and land-based spills causing massive air pollution plume and oil "lakes"

oil spills at sea, causing damage to marine wildlife, coral reefs, coastal wetlands

damage to deserts especially unexploded ordnance and mines

LONG-TERM ENVIRONMENTAL DAMAGE CAUSED BY WAR *1974-94*

significant war-related damage

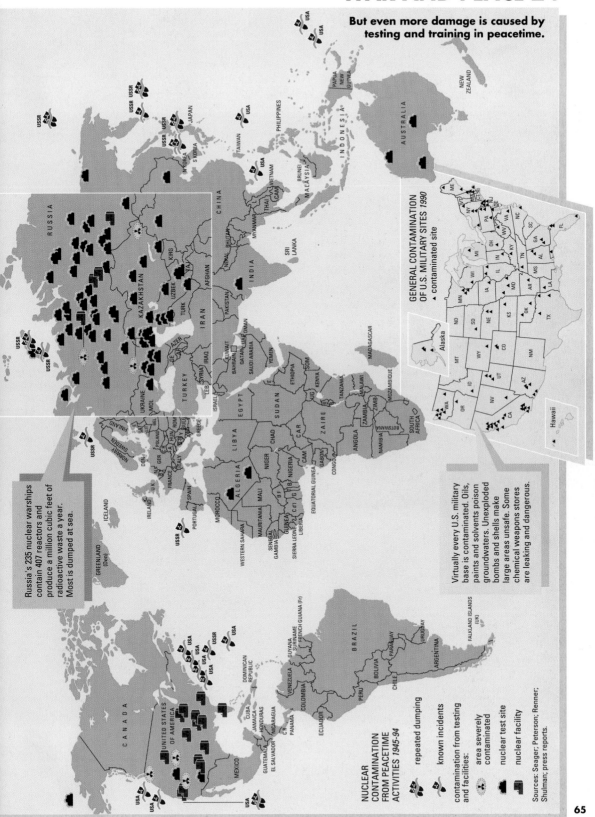

But even more damage is caused by testing and training in peacetime.

GENERAL CONTAMINATION OF U.S. MILITARY SITES *1990*
▲ contaminated site

Russia's 235 nuclear warships contain 407 reactors and produce a million cubic feet of radioactive waste a year. Most is dumped at sea.

Virtually every U.S. military base is contaminated. Oils, paints and solvents poison groundwaters. Unexploded bombs and shells make large areas unsafe. Some chemical weapons stores are leaking and dangerous.

NUCLEAR
CONTAMINATION
FROM PEACETIME
ACTIVITIES *1945-94*

repeated dumping

known incidents

contamination from testing and facilities:

area severely contaminated

nuclear test site

nuclear facility

Sources: Seager; Peterson; Renner; Shulman; press reports.

65

$720   red blunt nose viper
$1,500   olive python

$200   golden eagle
$2,500   bald eagle
$10,000   Peregrine falcon
$120,000   Gyrfalcon

$2,000   cockatoo
$30,000   Imperial Amazon macaw

$500   mountain lion
$3,500   tiger skin (Siberian)
$8,500   leopard
$14,000   snow leopard
$40,000   ocelot (coat)

$150,000   mountain gorilla

$15,000   Saguaro cactus

GOING RATES FOR INTERNATIONAL WILDLIFE
1990 US dollars

Source: *Environmental Almanac 1994*

THE STATE OF THE WORLD'S FISH STOCKS
early 1990s

fish stocks depleted
named species
salmon

fish stocks over-exploited
named species
shrimp

overfished areas
*exceeding maximum
sustainable yield*

areas of conflict between
local and foreign fishing fleets

Sources: FAO; *World Resources 1992-93;* press reports.

RUSSIA

KAZAKHSTAN

MONGOLIA

UZBEKISTAN
KIRGIS
TAJ
AFGHAN
PAKISTAN

N KOREA
S KOREA

CHINA

JAPAN

CANAD

ocean perch

king crabs

UNITED STAT
OF AMERIC

NEPAL
BHUTAN

INDIA

DESH MYANMAR
THAI
LAOS
CAM
VIETNAM

TAIWAN

salmon

PACIFIC
OCEAN

MEX

bluefin tuna

SRI LANKA

PHILIPPINES

shrimps

MALAYSIA

INDONESIA

PAPUA
NEW
GUINEA

shrimps

AUSTRALIA

NEW
ZEALAND

orange roughy

rock lobsters

The marine equivalent of tropical
rainforests, a single coral reef
may contain 3,000 species of
coral, fish and shellfish.

TURKEY
SY
IRAQ

LIBYA
EGYPT

MAURITANIA
MALI
NIGER
CHAD
SUDAN
SAUD

SEN
GUI
IV GH
NIGERIA
ETHIOP

LIBERIA
TOGO
CAM
CAR

GABON
ZAIRE
KENYA

TANZANIA

ANGOLA
ZAMBIA

NAMIBIA
BOTS
MOZ

SOUTH
AFRICA

**Eighty-five percent of the world's coral
communities are already damaged.**

Major threats to coral reefs:
pollution
sedimentation from coastal development
mining for building materials
tourism
blast fishing
boats and ships
ocean warming

THE STATE OF THE
WORLD'S CORAL REEFS
early 1990s

critical
loss imminent

threatened
loss likely in 20-40 years

stable

Source: Weber.

Life under the sea is almost as difficult as life on land. Nearly every commercial fish species is fully- or over-exploited and most of the world's coral reefs are threatened.

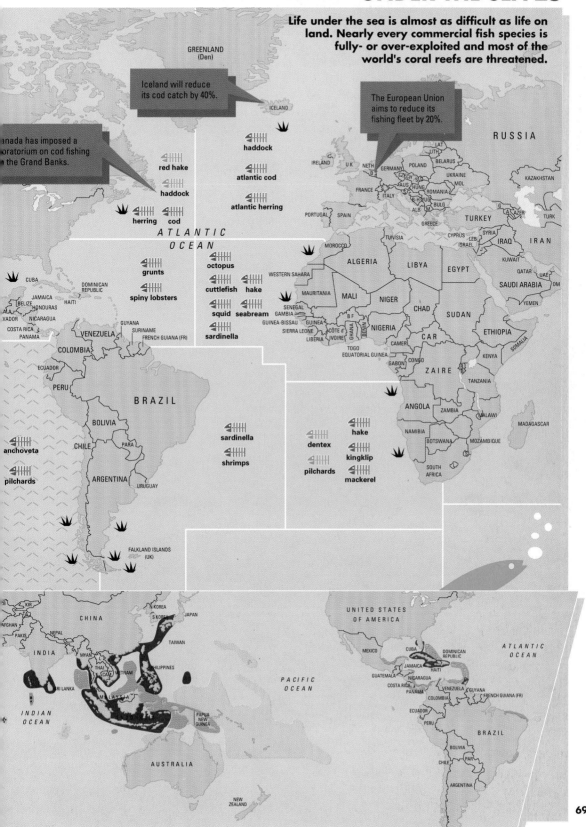

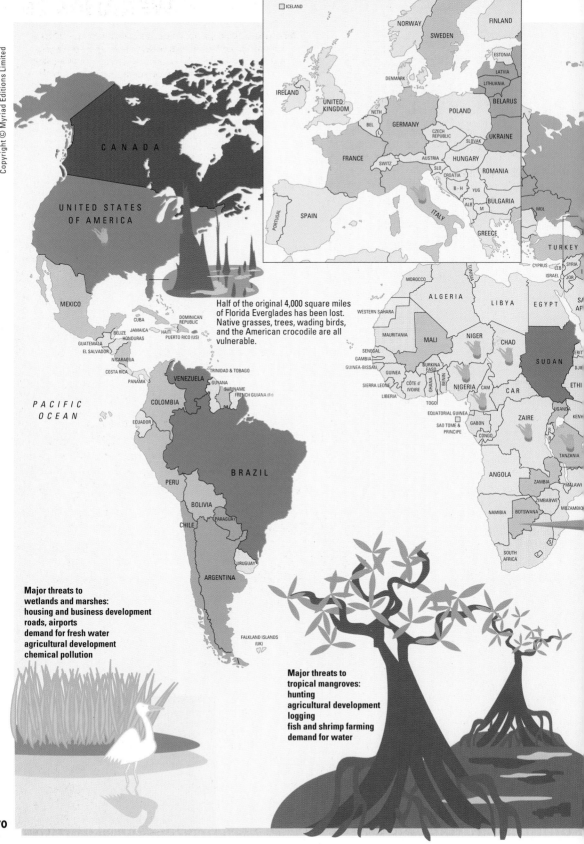

ICELAND

NORWAY
SWEDEN
FINLAND
DENMARK
ESTONIA
LATVIA
LITHUANIA
IRELAND
UNITED KINGDOM
NETH
BEL
GERMANY
CZECH REPUBLIC
SLOVAK
POLAND
BELARUS
UKRAINE
FRANCE
SWITZ
AUSTRIA
SLO
CROATIA
HUNGARY
ROMANIA
B - H
YUG
BULGARIA
ALB
M
PORTUGAL
SPAIN
ITALY
GREECE

CANADA

UNITED STATES
OF AMERICA

MEXICO

CUBA
BELIZE
JAMAICA
HAITI
DOMINICAN REPUBLIC
PUERTO RICO (US)
GUATEMALA
HONDURAS
EL SALVADOR
NICARAGUA
COSTA RICA
PANAMA

PACIFIC
OCEAN

Half of the original 4,000 square miles
of Florida Everglades has been lost.
Native grasses, trees, wading birds,
and the American crocodile are all
vulnerable.

VENEZUELA
TRINIDAD & TOBAGO
GUYANA
SURINAME
FRENCH GUIANA (Fr)
COLOMBIA

ECUADOR

PERU

BRAZIL

BOLIVIA

PARAGUAY

CHILE

ARGENTINA

URUGUAY

FALKLAND ISLANDS
(UK)

MOROCCO
ALGERIA
LIBYA
EGYPT
TUNISIA
WESTERN SAHARA
MAURITANIA
MALI
NIGER
CHAD
SUDAN
SENEGAL
GAMBIA
GUINEA-BISSAU
GUINEA
BURKINA FASO
BENIN
NIGERIA
CAM
CAR
ETHI
SIERRA LEONE
CÔTE d' IVOIRE
GHANA
TOGO
LIBERIA
EQUATORIAL GUINEA
SAO TOME & PRINCIPE
GABON
CONGO
ZAIRE
UGANDA
KENY
TANZANIA
ANGOLA
ZAMBIA
MALAWI
ZIMBABWE
MOZAMBIQUE
NAMIBIA
BOTSWANA
SOUTH AFRICA

TURKEY
CYPRUS
LEB
SYRIA
ISRAEL
JOR
MGL

**Major threats to
wetlands and marshes:**
housing and business development
roads, airports
demand for fresh water
agricultural development
chemical pollution

**Major threats to
tropical mangroves:**
hunting
agricultural development
logging
fish and shrimp farming
demand for water

The world's wetlands include swamps, marshes, wet prairies and tropical mangroves. Little documented, they are among the most richly productive ecosystems on earth.

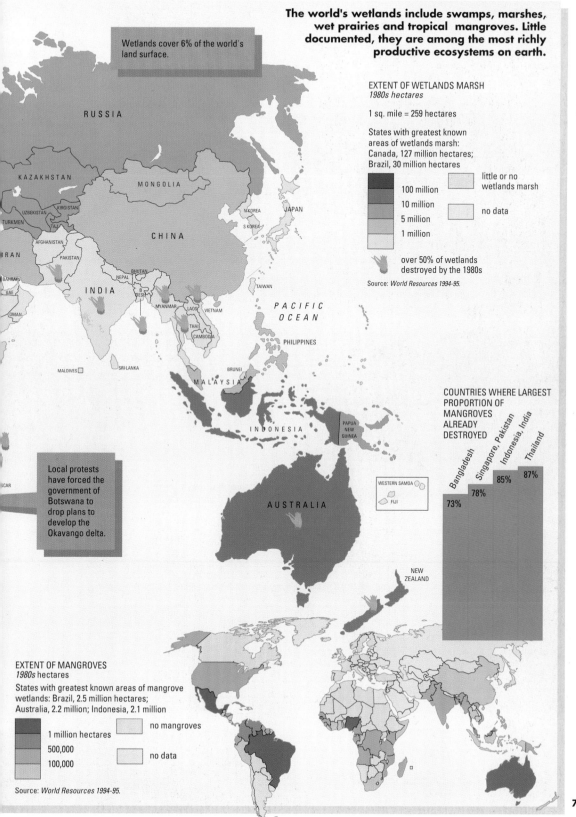

Wetlands cover 6% of the world's land surface.

EXTENT OF WETLANDS MARSH
1980s hectares

1 sq. mile = 259 hectares

States with greatest known areas of wetlands marsh: Canada, 127 million hectares; Brazil, 30 million hectares

- 100 million
- 10 million
- 5 million
- 1 million
- little or no wetlands marsh
- no data

over 50% of wetlands destroyed by the 1980s

Source: *World Resources 1994-95.*

COUNTRIES WHERE LARGEST PROPORTION OF MANGROVES ALREADY DESTROYED

Bangladesh	Singapore, Pakistan	Indonesia, India	Thailand
73%	78%	85%	87%

Local protests have forced the government of Botswana to drop plans to develop the Okavango delta.

EXTENT OF MANGROVES
1980s hectares

States with greatest known areas of mangrove wetlands: Brazil, 2.5 million hectares; Australia, 2.2 million; Indonesia, 2.1 million

- 1 million hectares
- 500,000
- 100,000
- no mangroves
- no data

Source: *World Resources 1994-95.*

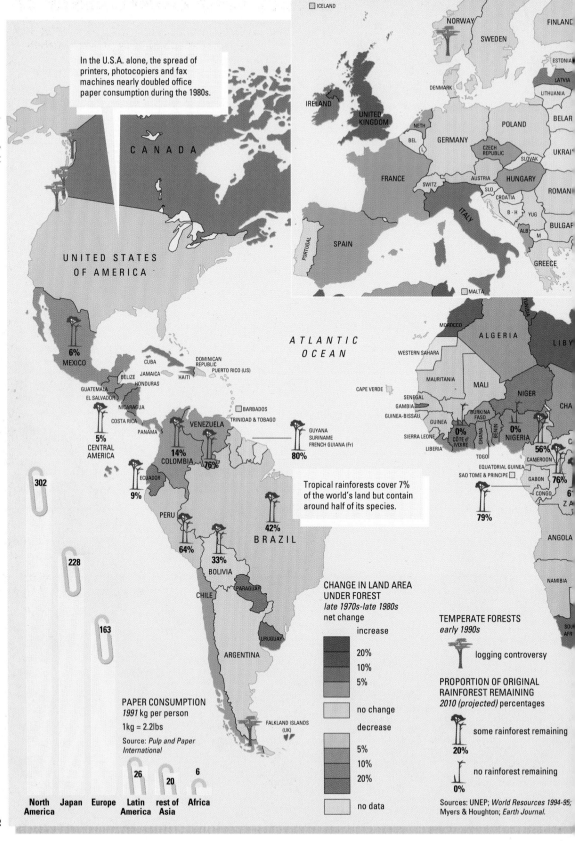

In the U.S.A. alone, the spread of printers, photocopiers and fax machines nearly doubled office paper consumption during the 1980s.

CANADA

UNITED STATES OF AMERICA

ICELAND

NORWAY
SWEDEN
FINLAND

IRELAND
UNITED KINGDOM
DENMARK
ESTONIA
LATVIA
LITHUANIA
BELAR

NETH
BEL
L
GERMANY
POLAND
UKRAI

FRANCE
CZECH REPUBLIC
SLOVAK
HUNGARY
AUSTRIA
SWITZ
SLO
CROATIA
B-H
YUG
ROMAN

PORTUGAL
SPAIN
ITALY
ALB
M
BULGAR

GREECE

MALTA

ATLANTIC OCEAN

6%
MEXICO

CUBA
JAMAICA
BELIZE
HONDURAS
GUATEMALA
EL SALVADOR
NICARAGUA
COSTA RICA
5%
CENTRAL AMERICA
PANAMA

DOMINICAN REPUBLIC
HAITI
PUERTO RICO (US)

BARBADOS
TRINIDAD & TOBAGO

CAPE VERDE

MOROCCO
WESTERN SAHARA
ALGERIA
LIBY

MAURITANIA
MALI
NIGER
CHA

SENEGAL
GAMBIA
GUINEA-BISSAU
GUINEA
SIERRA LEONE
LIBERIA
BURKINA FASO
0%
CÔTE d'IVOIRE
GHANA
BENIN
TOGO
0%
NIGERIA
56%
C

VENEZUELA
76%

GUYANA
SURINAME
FRENCH GUIANA (Fr)
80%

14%
COLOMBIA

ECUADOR
9%

CAMEROON
EQUATORIAL GUINEA
SAO TOME & PRINCIPE
GABON
76%
CONGO
6
ZA

79%

Tropical rainforests cover 7% of the world's land but contain around half of its species.

PERU
64%

42%
BRAZIL

33%
BOLIVIA

ANGOLA

302

228

163

CHILE
PARAGUAY

URUGUAY

ARGENTINA

NAMIBIA

SO
AF

CHANGE IN LAND AREA UNDER FOREST
late 1970s-late 1980s
net change

increase

20%
10%
5%

no change

decrease

5%
10%
20%

no data

TEMPERATE FORESTS
early 1990s

logging controversy

PROPORTION OF ORIGINAL RAINFOREST REMAINING
2010 (projected) percentages

some rainforest remaining
20%

no rainforest remaining
0%

PAPER CONSUMPTION
1991 kg per person

1kg = 2.2lbs

Source: *Pulp and Paper International*

FALKLAND ISLANDS (UK)

Sources: UNEP; *World Resources 1994-95;* Myers & Houghton; *Earth Journal.*

26
Latin America

20
rest of Asia

6
Africa

North America   Japan   Europe

As forests disappear, so does the habitat of a rich array of plants and wildlife.

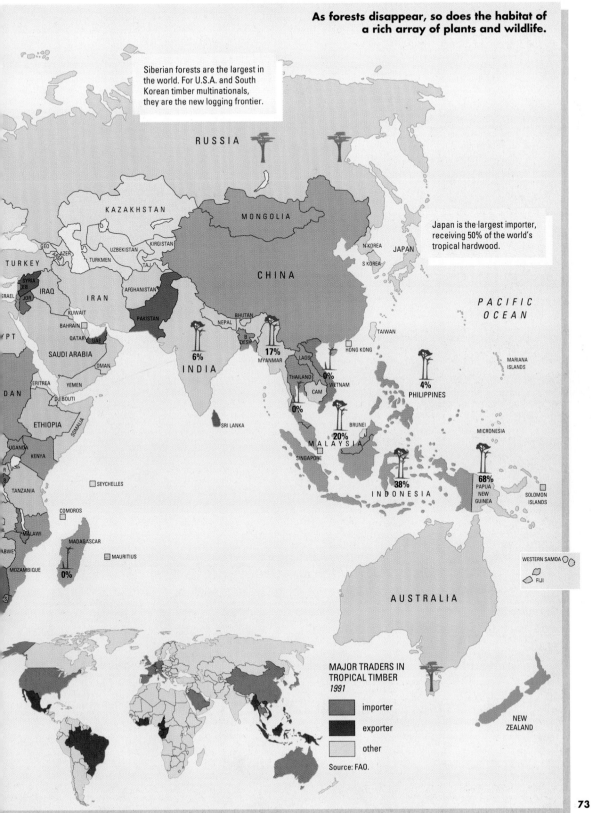

Siberian forests are the largest in the world. For U.S.A. and South Korean timber multinationals, they are the new logging frontier.

Japan is the largest importer, receiving 50% of the world's tropical hardwood.

RUSSIA

KAZAKHSTAN

MONGOLIA

GEO
AZER
TURKMEN
UZBEKISTAN
KIRGISTAN
TAJ

TURKEY

N KOREA
JAPAN
S KOREA

CHINA

SYRIA
LEB
JOR
ISRAEL
IRAQ
IRAN
AFGHANISTAN

KUWAIT
BAHRAIN
QATAR
UAE
OMAN

PAKISTAN
BHUTAN
NEPAL
B DESH

PACIFIC
OCEAN

TAIWAN

HONG KONG

SAUDI ARABIA

EGYPT

6%
INDIA

17%
MYANMAR

LAOS

0%
VIETNAM

THAILAND

CAM

MARIANA
ISLANDS

ERITREA
YEMEN
DJIBOUTI

SUDAN

SRI LANKA

0%

BRUNEI

4%
PHILIPPINES

ETHIOPIA
SOMALIA

UGANDA
KENYA

SEYCHELLES

20%
MALAYSIA

SINGAPORE

MICRONESIA

68%
PAPUA
NEW
GUINEA

SOLOMON
ISLANDS

TANZANIA

COMOROS

38%
INDONESIA

MALAWI

MADAGASCAR

MAURITIUS

WESTERN SAMOA

FIJI

MOZAMBIQUE

ZIMBABWE

0%

AUSTRALIA

MAJOR TRADERS IN TROPICAL TIMBER
1991

importer

exporter

other

Source: FAO.

NEW
ZEALAND

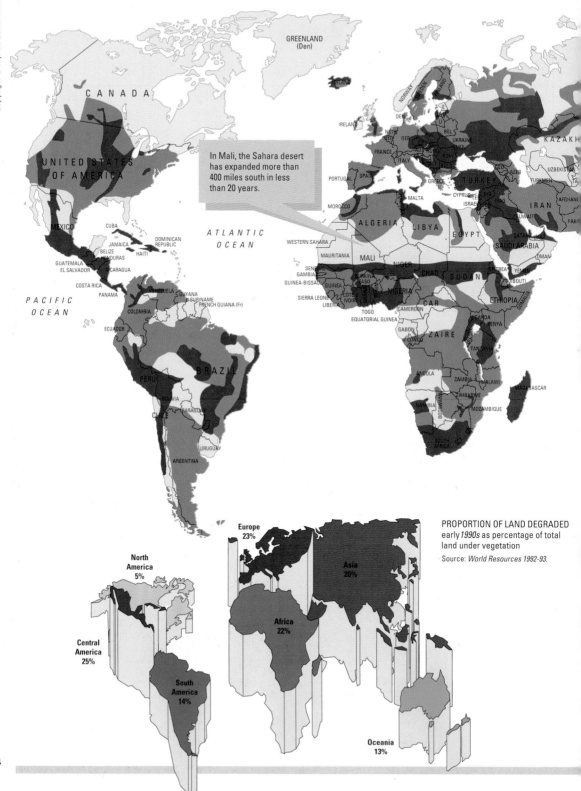

GREENLAND
(Den)

CANADA

UNITED STATES
OF AMERICA

In Mali, the Sahara desert
has expanded more than
400 miles south in less
than 20 years.

ATLANTIC
OCEAN

MEXICO

CUBA
JAMAICA
DOMINICAN
REPUBLIC
BELIZE
HONDURAS   HAITI
GUATEMALA
EL SALVADOR   NICARAGUA

COSTA RICA
PANAMA

PACIFIC
OCEAN

COLOMBIA

ECUADOR

VENEZUELA
GUYANA
SURINAME
FRENCH GUIANA (Fr)

BRAZIL

PERU

BOLIVIA

CHILE   PARAGUAY

URUGUAY

ARGENTINA

NORWAY SWEDEN

IRELAND   UK   DEN
NETH
BEL   GER
FRANCE   AUS   HUNG
ITALY

PORTUGAL   SPAIN

GREECE

MOROCCO

WESTERN SAHARA

MAURITANIA   MALI   NIGER

SENEGAL
GAMBIA
GUINEA-BISSAU
GUINEA   BURKINA
FASO
SIERRA LEONE   COTE
LIBERIA   D'IVOIRE   GHANA
TOGO
EQUATORIAL GUINEA
GABON
CONGO

UKRAINE

TURKEY

CYPRUS
ISRAEL

ALGERIA   LIBYA   EGYPT

MALTA

KAZAKH

UZBEKISTAN

AZER
GEO
SYR
IRAQ   IRAN
KUWAIT
QATAR
SAUDI ARABIA   UAE
OMAN

TURKMEN

AFGHANI

PAKIS

CHAD   SUDAN   ERITREA   YEMEN
DJIBOUTI
NIGERIA
CAR   ETHIOPIA
CAMEROON   SOMALIA
UGANDA   KENYA
ZAIRE   TANZANIA

ANGOLA   ZAMBIA   MALAWI   MADAGASCAR
ZIMBABWE
NAMIBIA   BOTSWANA   MOZAMBIQUE

SOUTH
AFRICA

North
America
5%

Central
America
25%

Europe
23%

South
America
14%

Africa
22%

Asia
20%

Oceania
13%

PROPORTION OF LAND DEGRADED
early *1990s* as percentage of total
land under vegetation

Source: *World Resources 1992-93.*

Soil is essentially a non-renewable resource, which is now being lost at an accelerating rate.

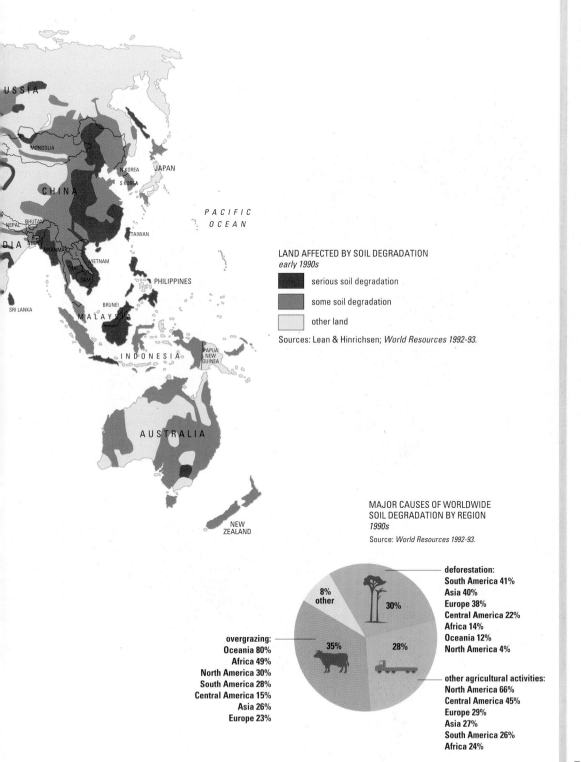

LAND AFFECTED BY SOIL DEGRADATION
early 1990s

serious soil degradation

some soil degradation

other land

Sources: Lean & Hinrichsen; *World Resources 1992-93.*

MAJOR CAUSES OF WORLDWIDE SOIL DEGRADATION BY REGION
1990s

Source: *World Resources 1992-93.*

8% other

30%

35%

28%

deforestation:
South America 41%
Asia 40%
Europe 38%
Central America 22%
Africa 14%
Oceania 12%
North America 4%

overgrazing:
Oceania 80%
Africa 49%
North America 30%
South America 28%
Central America 15%
Asia 26%
Europe 23%

other agricultural activities:
North America 66%
Central America 45%
Europe 29%
Asia 27%
South America 26%
Africa 24%

75

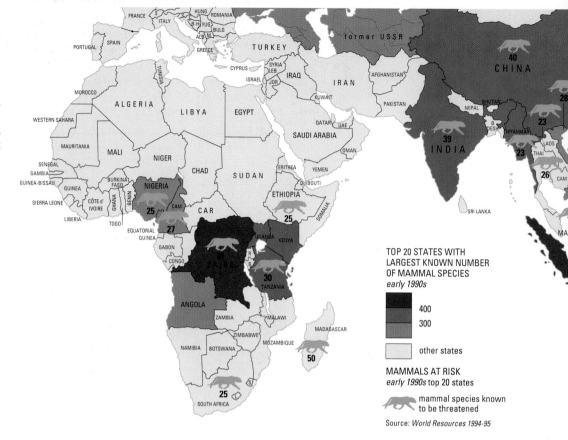

Copyright © Myriad Editions Limited

TOP 20 STATES WITH
LARGEST KNOWN NUMBER
OF MAMMAL SPECIES
early 1990s

400
300
other states

MAMMALS AT RISK
early 1990s top 20 states

mammal species known
to be threatened

Source: *World Resources 1994-95*

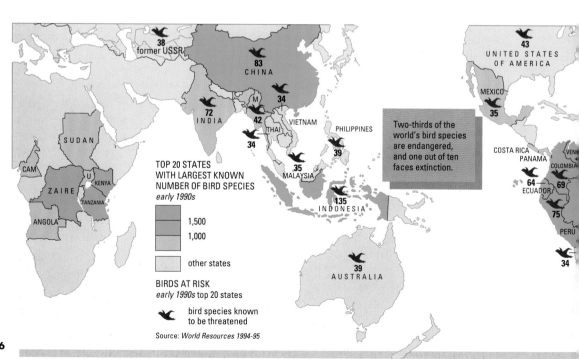

TOP 20 STATES
WITH LARGEST KNOWN
NUMBER OF BIRD SPECIES
early 1990s

1,500
1,000
other states

BIRDS AT RISK
early 1990s top 20 states

bird species known
to be threatened

Source: *World Resources 1994-95*

Two-thirds of the
world's bird species
are endangered,
and one out of ten
faces extinction.

By the year 2050, half of all the species alive today could be extinct.

JAPAN

REA

REA

TAIWAN

MARIANA
ISLANDS

PHILIPPINES

MICRONESIA

49
INDONESIA

PAPUA
NEW
GUINEA

38
AUSTRALIA

FIJI

NEW
ZEALAND

UNITED STATES
OF AMERICA
27

25
MEXICO

*ATLANTIC
OCEAN*

CUBA
JAMAICA
BELIZE
HONDURAS
GUATEMALA
EL SALVADOR
NICARAGUA
COSTA RICA
PANAMA

DOMINICAN
REPUBLIC
HAITI
ST KITTS NEVIS
& ANGUILLA
ANTIGUA & BARBUDA

*PACIFIC
OCEAN*

VENEZUELA
GUYANA
SURINAME
FRENCH GUIANA (Fr)

25
COLOMBIA

ECUADOR

29
PERU

40
BRAZIL

BOLIVIA

PARAGUAY

CHILE

URUGUAY

23
ARGENTINA

FALKLAND ISLANDS
(UK)

Fifty plant species become extinct every day. Small islands in the Pacific, Atlantic and Indian Oceans harbor the largest numbers of rare and threatened plants.

The numbers of species threatened are seriously underestimated. Probably only 50% of mammals and 20% of reptiles have been reviewed.

LOSS OF WILD HABITAT *mid-1980s*
percentages of original area lost, selected states

Source: International Union for the Conservation of Nature

Vietnam 80%
Côte d'Ivoire, Philippines 79%
Madagascar 75%
Myanmar 71%
Ethiopia 70%
Cameroon 59%
South Africa 57%
Indonesia 49%
Malaysia 41%

REPTILES AT RISK *late 1980s*

Known world total: 4,771
Threatened: 169, or 4%

Source: *World Resources 1994-95.*

23
AZIL

NTINA

53

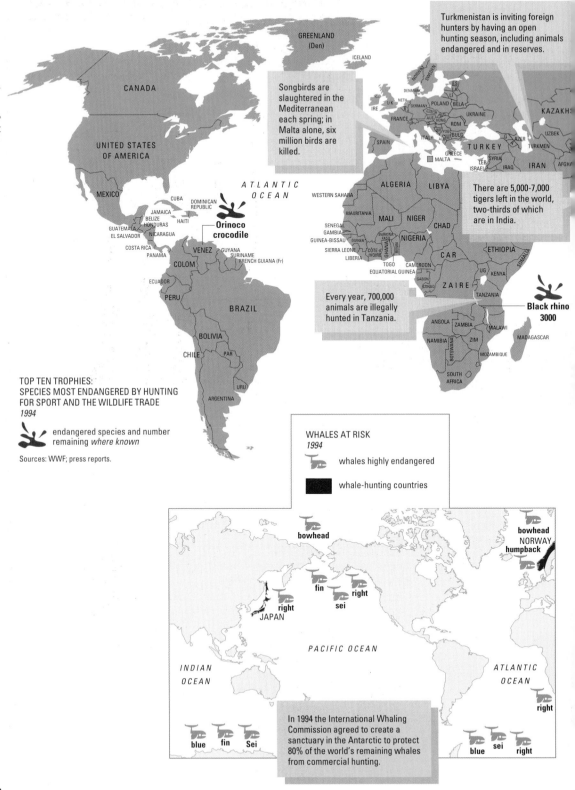

Turkmenistan is inviting foreign hunters by having an open hunting season, including animals endangered and in reserves.

Songbirds are slaughtered in the Mediterranean each spring; in Malta alone, six million birds are killed.

There are 5,000-7,000 tigers left in the world, two-thirds of which are in India.

Orinoco crocodile

Every year, 700,000 animals are illegally hunted in Tanzania.

Black rhino 3000

TOP TEN TROPHIES:
SPECIES MOST ENDANGERED BY HUNTING FOR SPORT AND THE WILDLIFE TRADE
1994

endangered species and number remaining *where known*

Sources: WWF; press reports.

WHALES AT RISK
1994

whales highly endangered

whale-hunting countries

bowhead

bowhead NORWAY humpback

fin

right

right

sei

right

JAPAN

PACIFIC OCEAN

INDIAN OCEAN

ATLANTIC OCEAN

right

In 1994 the International Whaling Commission agreed to create a sanctuary in the Antarctic to protect 80% of the world's remaining whales from commercial hunting.

blue   fin   Sei

blue   sei   right

Hunting for sport or profit is one of the greatest threats to the world's animals.

USSIA

Siberian tiger
500

MONGOLIA

Asiatic black bear

N KOREA

JAPAN

S KOREA

al tiger
1000

CHINA

Giant panda
1000

EPAL BHUTAN

B
DESH MYAN

TAIWAN

IA

SRI LANKA

BRUNEI

MALAYSIA

PHILIPPINES

Moluccan
cockatoo

Hawksbill
sea turtle

Orangutan

INDONESIA

PAPUA
NEW
GUINEA

Sumatran rhino
700

Orangutan

AUSTRALIA

NEW
ZEALAND

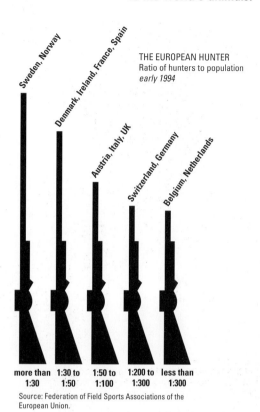

THE EUROPEAN HUNTER
Ratio of hunters to population
early 1994

| more than 1:30 | 1:30 to 1:50 | 1:50 to 1:100 | 1:200 to 1:300 | less than 1:300 |

Sweden, Norway

Denmark, Ireland, France, Spain

Austria, Italy, UK

Switzerland, Germany

Belgium, Netherlands

Source: Federation of Field Sports Associations of the European Union.

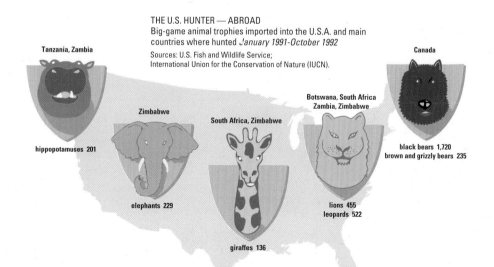

THE U.S. HUNTER — ABROAD
Big-game animal trophies imported into the U.S.A. and main
countries where hunted *January 1991-October 1992*

Sources: U.S. Fish and Wildlife Service;
International Union for the Conservation of Nature (IUCN).

Tanzania, Zambia

Canada

Zimbabwe

Botswana, South Africa
Zambia, Zimbabwe

South Africa, Zimbabwe

hippopotamuses 201

black bears 1,720
brown and grizzly bears 235

elephants 229

lions 455
leopards 522

giraffes 136

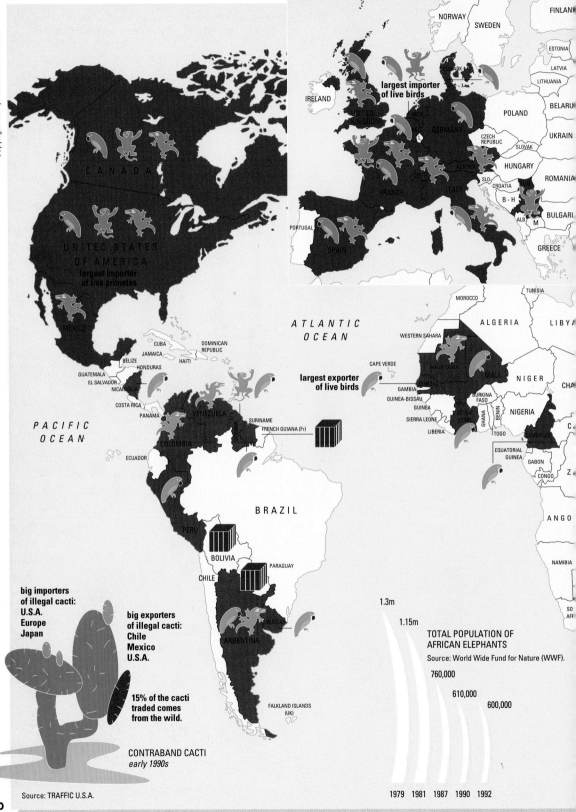

largest importer of live birds

NORWAY
SWEDEN
FINLAN
ESTONIA
LATVIA
LITHUANIA
IRELAND
BELARU
UNITED KINGDOM
POLAND
GERMANY
UKRAIN
CZECH REPUBLIC
SLOVAK
HUNGARY
AUSTRIA
ROMANIA
FRANCE
ITALY
CROATIA
B - H
BULGARI
PORTUGAL
SPAIN
ALB
M
GREECE

C A N A D A

U N I T E D   S T A T E S
O F   A M E R I C A
largest importer
of live primates

MEXICO

CUBA
DOMINICAN REPUBLIC
JAMAICA
HAITI

A T L A N T I C
O C E A N

TUNISIA
MOROCCO
WESTERN SAHARA
ALGERIA
LIBYA

CAPE VERDE
**largest exporter
of live birds**
MAURITANIA
MALI
NIGER
CHA

BELIZE
HONDURAS
GUATEMALA
EL SALVADOR
NICARAGUA
COSTA RICA
PANAMA

GAMBIA
GUINEA-BISSAU
GUINEA
SIERRA LEONE
LIBERIA
BURKINA FASO
CÔTE d'IVOIRE
GHANA
TOGO
BENIN
NIGERIA
CAMEROON
EQUATORIAL GUINEA

P A C I F I C
O C E A N

VENEZUELA
GUYANA
COLOMBIA
SURINAME
FRENCH GUIANA (Fr)
ECUADOR

GABON
CONGO
Z

B R A Z I L

A N G O

PERU
BOLIVIA
PARAGUAY
CHILE

NAMIBIA

**big importers
of illegal cacti:
U.S.A.
Europe
Japan**

**big exporters
of illegal cacti:
Chile
Mexico
U.S.A.**

URUGUAY
ARGENTINA

1.3m

1.15m

SO
AFI

**TOTAL POPULATION OF
AFRICAN ELEPHANTS**
Source: World Wide Fund for Nature (WWF).

760,000

**15% of the cacti
traded comes
from the wild.**

FALKLAND ISLANDS
(UK)

610,000
600,000

CONTRABAND CACTI
early 1990s

1979 1981 1987 1990 1992

Source: TRAFFIC U.S.A.

The world trade in wild animals, their skins and their tusks is a major industry worth U.S. $5 billion. Much of this trade is legal, even more is not.

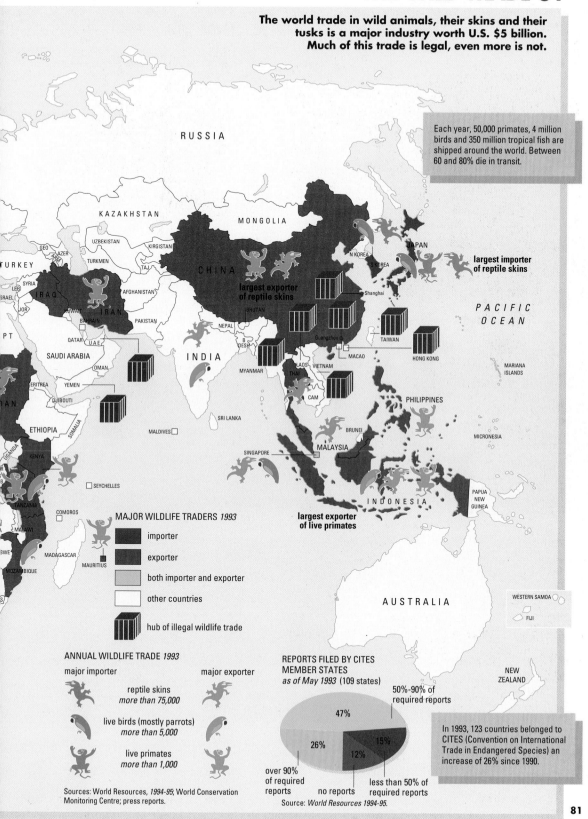

Each year, 50,000 primates, 4 million birds and 350 million tropical fish are shipped around the world. Between 60 and 80% die in transit.

largest importer of reptile skins

largest exporter of reptile skins

largest exporter of live primates

MAJOR WILDLIFE TRADERS *1993*

- importer
- exporter
- both importer and exporter
- other countries
- hub of illegal wildlife trade

ANNUAL WILDLIFE TRADE *1993*

major importer		major exporter
	reptile skins *more than 75,000*	
	live birds (mostly parrots) *more than 5,000*	
	live primates *more than 1,000*	

Sources: World Resources, *1994-95*; World Conservation Monitoring Centre; press reports.

REPORTS FILED BY CITES MEMBER STATES
as of May 1993 (109 states)

50%-90% of required reports

47%

26%

12%

15%

over 90% of required reports

no reports

less than 50% of required reports

Source: *World Resources 1994-95.*

In 1993, 123 countries belonged to CITES (Convention on International Trade in Endangered Species) an increase of 26% since 1990.

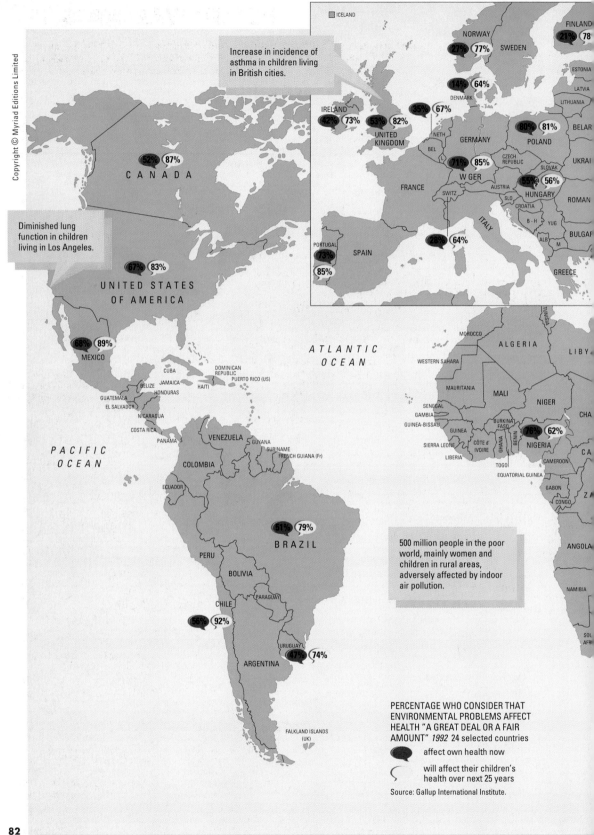

Increase in incidence of asthma in children living in British cities.

Diminished lung function in children living in Los Angeles.

500 million people in the poor world, mainly women and children in rural areas, adversely affected by indoor air pollution.

PERCENTAGE WHO CONSIDER THAT ENVIRONMENTAL PROBLEMS AFFECT HEALTH "A GREAT DEAL OR A FAIR AMOUNT" *1992* 24 selected countries

affect own health now

will affect their children's health over next 25 years

Source: Gallup International Institute.

There are many signs that environmental problems contribute to human ill-health. Some doctors and scientists dismiss these warnings as alarmist; others suggest we are not alarmist enough.

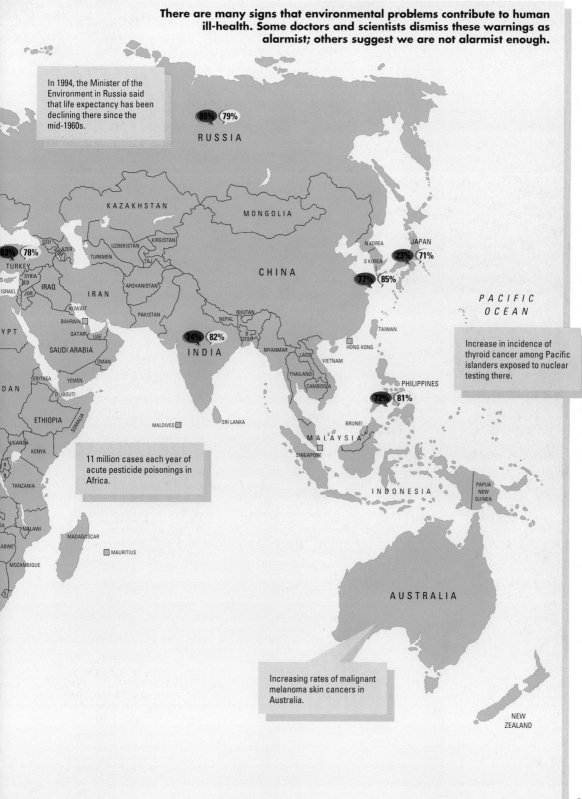

In 1994, the Minister of the Environment in Russia said that life expectancy has been declining there since the mid-1960s.

RUSSIA

89% 79%

KAZAKHSTAN

MONGOLIA

GEO
63% 78%
TURKEY
AZER
UZBEKISTAN KIRGISTAN
TURKMEN
TAJ.
SYRIA
LEB
ISRAEL JOR IRAQ
IRAN
AFGHANISTAN
KUWAIT
BAHRAIN
QATAR UAE
PAKISTAN

CHINA

N KOREA
JAPAN
23% 71%
S KOREA
77% 85%

PACIFIC OCEAN

Y P T
SAUDI ARABIA
OMAN
YEMEN

NEPAL
BHUTAN
74% 82%
INDIA
B DESH
MYANMAR
LAOS
VIETNAM
THAILAND
CAMBODIA

TAIWAN

HONG KONG

PHILIPPINES
72% 81%

Increase in incidence of thyroid cancer among Pacific islanders exposed to nuclear testing there.

D A N
ERITREA
DJIBOUTI
ETHIOPIA
SOMALIA
UGANDA
KENYA

MALDIVES
SRI LANKA

BRUNEI
MALAYSIA
SINGAPORE

11 million cases each year of acute pesticide poisonings in Africa.

TANZANIA

INDONESIA

PAPUA NEW GUINEA

MALAWI
MADAGASCAR
ABWE
MOZAMBIQUE
MAURITIUS

AUSTRALIA

Increasing rates of malignant melanoma skin cancers in Australia.

NEW ZEALAND

Antarctic Treaty 1959 and 1980
39 states

Ramsar Convention on Wetlands 1971
81 states

London Dumping Convention 1972
82 states

Convention on International
Trade in Endangered Species.(CITES) 1973
123 states

Basel Convention on Hazardous Waste 1989
57 states

Biodiversity Treaty 1992
160 states

Climate Change Treaty 1992
163 states

NUMBER OF STATES WHO HAVE SIGNED
AND/OR RATIFIED INTERNATIONAL CONVENTIONS
TO PROTECT THE ENVIRONMENT
as of 1993

Source: OECD; *World Resources 1994-95*

NORWAY ④
SWEDEN ③
FINLAND ②
DENMARK ③
ESTONIA
LATVIA
LITHUANIA
IRELAND ①
UNITED KINGDOM ⑭
NETH
BELGIUM
POLAND
Wieliczka Salt Mines ⑥
BELARUS ①
GERMANY ⑬
CZECH REPUBLIC ③
③
UKRAINE ①
SLOVAK
FRANCE ⑳
SWITZ
AUSTRIA ①
② HUNG
SLO
ITALY ⑧
CROATIA ③
YUG ④
ROMANIA ④ ⑨
B-H
Plitvice Lakes National Park
Dubrovnik Old City
Kotor Region ④
M
BULG ④
PORTUGAL ⑥
SPAIN ⑳
ALBANIA
GREECE ⑬
Srebarna Nature Reserve ① ①
③
MALTA

C A N A D A ⑩

UNITED STATES OF AMERICA ⑱

MEXICO ⑬

Everglades National Park

BAHAMAS ②
CUBA
DOMINICAN REPUBLIC ①
PUERTO RICO (US) ①
JAMAICA
HAITI
BELIZE
HONDURAS
GUATEMALA ③
EL SALVADOR ①
NICARAGUA
DOMINICA ①
ST LUCIA
BARBADOS
GRENADA
TRINIDAD & TOBAGO
COSTA RICA
PANAMA ①
VENEZUELA ①
GUYANA
SURINAME
FRENCH GUIANA (Fr)
COLOMBIA ③

A T L A N T I C   O C E A N

MOROCCO ③
TUNISIA ⑦
LIBYA ⑤
WESTERN SAHARA
ALGERIA ⑦
Air-Ténéré National Nature Reserve
Timbuktu
CAPE VERDE ISLANDS ③
MAURITANIA ①
MALI ③
NIGER ①
CHAD
SENEGAL ③
GAMBIA
GUINEA-BISSAU ①
GUINEA
BURKINA FASO ①
NIGERIA ①
Mount Nimba Nature Reserve
SIERRA LEONE
IVORY COAST ②
BENIN ①
LIBERIA ③
GHANA
TOGO
Royal Palaces of Abomey
CAMEROON ①
GABON
CONGO ④
ZA

PACIFIC OCEAN

ECUADOR ③
Sangay National Park
Chan Chan Archaeological Zone

PERU ⑧
BRAZIL ⑧
BOLIVIA ③
PARAGUAY ①
CHILE
URUGUAY ③
ARGENTINA ③
FALKLAND ISLANDS (UK)

ANGOLA
NAMIBIA
SOUTH AFRICA

Proposed mining development in Guinea and influx of refugees from Liberia.

Damaged by tornado in 1985.

Proposed highway construction, heavy poaching, and illegal livestock grazing.

Many World Heritage sites also protect threatened species, such as the Royal Chitwan National Park in Nepal, which protects the Bengal tiger.

Some of the world's unique places — from national monuments to natural habitats — are protected, but many poorly so.

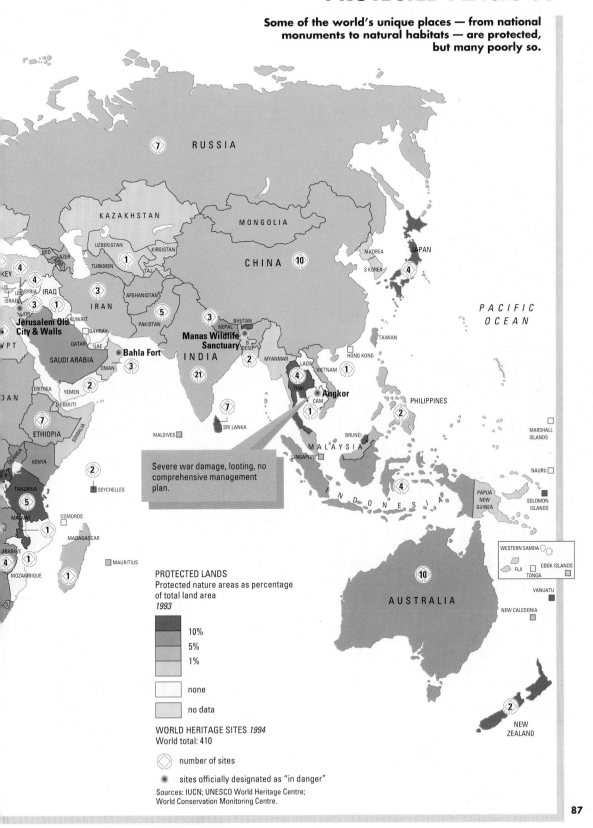

RUSSIA ⑦

KAZAKHSTAN

MONGOLIA

UZBEKISTAN ①
KIRGISTAN
TURKMEN
TAJ.

CHINA ⑩

N.KOREA
S.KOREA

JAPAN ④

PACIFIC OCEAN

GEO
AZER
KEY ④
④
LEB SYRIA IRAQ
ISRAEL
③ ①
IRAN ③
AFGHANISTAN
PAKISTAN ⑤

Jerusalem Old City & Walls

KUWAIT
BAHRAIN
QATAR UAE
OMAN

Bahla Fort

SAUDI ARABIA ③

Manas Wildlife Sanctuary ③

NEPAL BHUTAN
B DESH
INDIA ②

MYANMAR
LAOS
THAI ④
VIETNAM ①

TAIWAN
HONG KONG

② ①
② ②

Angkor ①
CAM

PHILIPPINES ②

ERITREA
YEMEN ②
DJIBOUTI

②①
JOR

PT

ETHIOPIA ⑦

SOMALIA

② SEYCHELLES

MALDIVES

SRI LANKA ⑦

BRUNEI

MALAYSIA

SINGAPORE

INDONESIA ④

MARSHALL ISLANDS

NAURU

PAPUA NEW GUINEA ④

SOLOMON ISLANDS

Severe war damage, looting, no comprehensive management plan.

UGANDA
KENYA ②

COMOROS

MADAGASCAR

TANZANIA ⑤

MALAWI ①

MAURITIUS

WESTERN SAMOA
FIJI
TONGA
COOK ISLANDS

VANUATU

NEW CALEDONIA

AUSTRALIA ⑩

BABWE ④
MOZAMBIQUE ①

①

NEW ZEALAND ②

PROTECTED LANDS
Protected nature areas as percentage of total land area
1993

- 10%
- 5%
- 1%
- none
- no data

WORLD HERITAGE SITES *1994*
World total: 410

⬡ number of sites

🔴 sites officially designated as "in danger"

Sources: IUCN; UNESCO World Heritage Centre; World Conservation Monitoring Centre.

In the U.S.A. in 1980, Greenpeace had 250,000 members; by 1990, the number had risen to 2.5 million.

CANADA
61%
28% 79%

UNITED STATES OF AMERICA
65%
45% 66%

MEXICO
59%
56% 70%

NORWAY SWEDEN
72%
12% 88%

FINLAND
ESTONIA
LATVIA
LITHUANIA

IRELAND
UNITED KINGDOM
70%
36% 76%

DENMARK

NETH
BEL
GERMANY
88% 73%

CZECH REPUBLIC
POLAND
49%
BELARUS
UKRAIN
SLO

FRANCE
SWITZ
AUSTRIA
HUNGARY
SLO
ROMANIA
49%
72% 71%

ITALY
70%
27% 86%

YUG
ALB
M
BULGA
GREECE

PORTUGAL
SPAIN

MALTA

ATLANTIC OCEAN

TUNISIA
MOROCCO
ALGERIA
LIBYA
WESTERN SAHARA
MAURITANIA
MALI
NIGER
CHAD
SENEGAL
GAMBIA
GUINEA-BISSAU
GUINEA
BURKINA FASO
BENIN
NIGERIA
28%
38% 24%
SIERRA LEONE
CÔTE d'IVOIRE
GHANA
CAR
LIBERIA
TOGO
EQUATORIAL GUINEA
CAMEROON
GABON
ZA
CONGO

CUBA
DOMINICAN REPUBLIC
PUERTO RICO (US)
BELIZE
JAMAICA
HAITI
HONDURAS
GUATEMALA
EL SALVADOR
NICARAGUA
GRENADA
COSTA RICA
PANAMA
VENEZUELA
GUYANA
SURINAME
FRENCH GUIANA (Fr)
COLOMBIA
ECUADOR

PACIFIC OCEAN

BRAZIL
53%
49% 64%

PERU
BOLIVIA
PARAGUAY
64%
68% 88%
CHILE

ANGOLA
NAMIBIA
SOUT AFRIC

URUGUAY
54%
37% 74%
ARGENTINA

SHARES OF THE ENVIRONMENTAL CLEAN-UP BUSINESS, WESTERN EUROPE
1992 percentages
Source: *The Economist*

- 33% solid/hazardous waste management
- 24% water treatment
- 15% air pollution control
- 11% recycling
- 7% engineering
- 7% waste management equipment
- 3% other

RISE IN UK MEMBERSHIP OF GREEN ORGANIZATIONS
1980 to 1991
Sources: McCormick; *The Economist.*

Friends of the Earth
1980 12,000
1991 240,000

WWF
1980 51,000
1991 230,000

Greenpeace
1980 10,000
1991 411,000

By the early 1990s, public opinion had moved towards support of the environment's special needs — and the clean-up business began to look profitable.

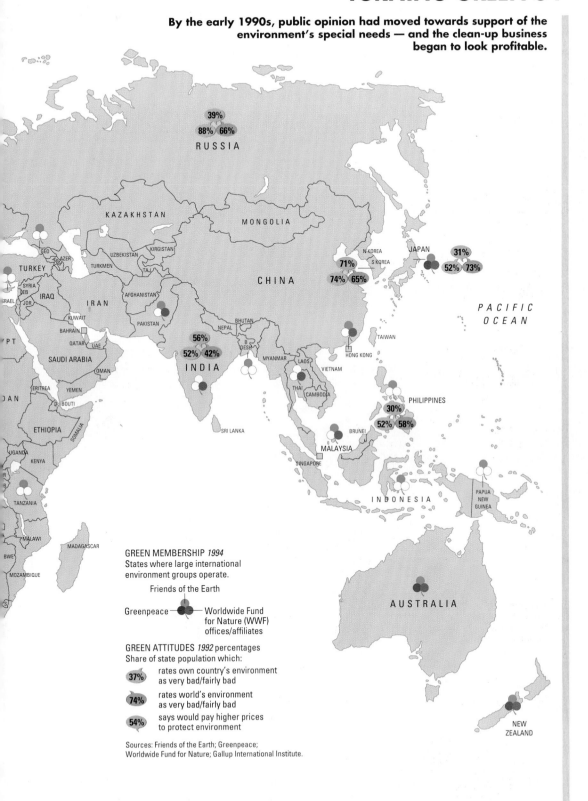

RUSSIA 39% 88% 66%

KAZAKHSTAN

MONGOLIA

UZBEKISTAN KIRGISTAN

TURKMEN TAJ

AFGHANISTAN

CHINA

N-KOREA
S KOREA 71% 74% 65%

JAPAN 31% 52% 73%

PACIFIC OCEAN

GEO AZER

TURKEY

SYRIA
LEB
ISRAEL JOR IRAQ

IRAN

PAKISTAN

KUWAIT

BAHRAIN

QATAR
UAE

SAUDI ARABIA

OMAN

NEPAL
BHUTAN
B
DESH

INDIA 56% 52% 42%

MYANMAR LAOS

TAIWAN

HONG KONG

VIETNAM

THAI CAMBODIA

ERITREA

YEMEN

DAN

DJIBOUTI

ETHIOPIA

SOMALIA

SRI LANKA

MALAYSIA

SINGAPORE

BRUNEI

PHILIPPINES 30% 52% 58%

UGANDA KENYA

INDONESIA

PAPUA NEW GUINEA

TANZANIA

MALAWI

MADAGASCAR

BWE

MOZAMBIQUE

AUSTRALIA

GREEN MEMBERSHIP *1994*
States where large international environment groups operate.

Friends of the Earth

Greenpeace ——— Worldwide Fund for Nature (WWF) offices/affiliates

GREEN ATTITUDES *1992* percentages
Share of state population which:

37% rates own country's environment as very bad/fairly bad

74% rates world's environment as very bad/fairly bad

54% says would pay higher prices to protect environment

Sources: Friends of the Earth; Greenpeace; Worldwide Fund for Nature; Gallup International Institute.

NEW ZEALAND

World Bank loans for projects with "primarily environmental objectives" almost tripled between 1990 and 1993.

ATLANTIC OCEAN

PACIFIC OCEAN

EXTERNAL DEBT OF LOW AND MODERATE INCOME STATES
1993

- severely indebted
- moderately indebted
- less indebted
- other states or no data

DEBT-FOR-NATURE SWAPS
1987-93

debt written off in exchange for investment in environmental projects
number of transactions given

Source: World Bank.

GLOBAL ENVIRONMENT FACILITY (GEF)
shares of total pledged by donor states *1993-94*
total: U.S. $2 billion

The GEF was set up in 1991 to fund projects in developing countries designed to tackle global environmental problems, such as climate change and loss of biodiversity.

Source: UNEP; U.S. Treasury Department.

GEF projects, 1991-93: biodiversity 42%; global warming 41%; international waters 16%; ozone, below 1%.

S. Korea, New Zealand, Portugal, Spain, Ireland, Australia, Austria, Finland, Norway
Denmark, Switzerland
Sweden
Canada, Netherlands
Italy
France, UK
Germany
Japan
U.S.A.

total pledge by recipients:
Bangladesh, Brazil, China,
Côte d'Ivoire, Egypt, India

below 1% | 1% | 2% | 3% | 4% | 6% | 7% | 12% | 16% | 21% | 2.5%

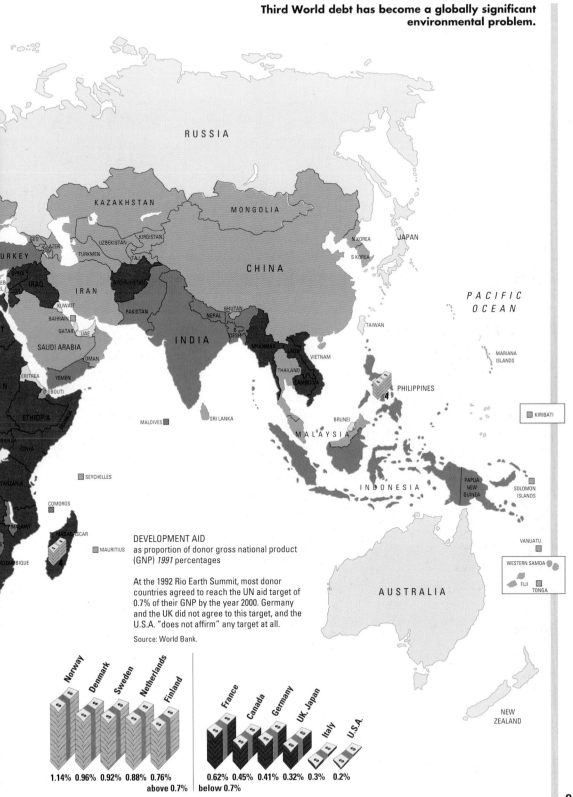

Third World debt has become a globally significant environmental problem.

DEVELOPMENT AID
as proportion of donor gross national product
(GNP) *1991* percentages

At the 1992 Rio Earth Summit, most donor
countries agreed to reach the UN aid target of
0.7% of their GNP by the year 2000. Germany
and the UK did not agree to this target, and the
U.S.A. "does not affirm" any target at all.

Source: World Bank.

Norway 1.14% Denmark 0.96% Sweden 0.92% Netherlands 0.88% Finland 0.76%
above 0.7%

France 0.62% Canada 0.45% Germany 0.41% UK 0.32% Japan 0.3% Italy 0.3% U.S.A. 0.2%
below 0.7%

	1 Population 1995 millions	2 Percentage of total population which is urban 1995	3 Percentage of household income spent on food 1980-85	4 Number of cars 1991 thousands	5 CO₂ emissi from indust processes 1 thousand metri
Afghanistan	23.2	20.0%	–	38.0	5,148
Albania	3.4	37.3%	–	–	6,247
Algeria	28.6	55.8%	–	760.0	55,194
Angola	11.1	32.2%	–	120.0	4,789
Argentina	34.3	87.5%	35%	4,335.3	115,848
Armenia	3.7	–	–	–	–
Australia	18.3	85.2%	13%	7,734.1	261,818
Austria	7.9	60.6%	16%	3,100.0	60,331
Azerbaijan	7.5	–	–	–	–
Bahamas	0.3	–	–	70.0	–
Bahrain	0.5	–	–	102.4	–
Bangladesh	128.6	19.5%	59%	67.0	15,444
Barbados	0.3	–	–	44.3	–
Belarus	10.3	–	–	–	–
Belgium	10.0	96.7%	15%	3,928.9	102,679
Belize	0.2	52.5%	–	2.0	264
Benin	5.4	41.8%	37%	25.0	561
Bhutan	1.7	6.4%	–	–	128
Bolivia	8.1	54.4%	33%	265.0	5,855
Botswana	1.4	30.9%	25%	25.0	2,154
Brazil	161.4	78.7%	35%	12,283.9	215,601
Brunei	0.3	–	–	115.5	–
Bulgaria	8.9	70.7%	–	1,316.6	56,675
Burkina Faso	10.4	19.5%	–	12.5	557
Burundi	6.3	6.1%	–	8.5	220
Cambodia	9.5	12.9%	–	–	462
Cameroon	13.3	44.9%	24%	94.0	1,924
Canada	28.6	78.1%	11%	13,061.1	410,628
Central African Rep.	3.4	50.8%	–	–	209
Chad	6.4	37.0%	–	8.5	253
Chile	14.2	85.9%	29%	715.0	32,525
China	1,238.3	30.3%	61%	1,764.9	2,543,380
Colombia	35.1	72.7%	29%	798.6	57,503
Comoros	0.6	–	–	–	–
Congo	2.6	43.4%	37%	27.0	2,015
Cook Islands	<0.1	–	–	–	–
Costa Rica	3.4	49.7%	33%	168.8	3,250
Côte d'Ivoire	14.4	43.6%	39%	170.0	6,379
Croatia	4.8	–	–	–	–
Cuba	11.1	76.0%	–	–	34,398
Cyprus	0.7	–	–	187.7	–
Czech Republic	10.3	–	–	–	–
Denmark	5.2	85.5%	13%	1,593.0	63,054

Sources: Col 1: World Resources 1994-95; UNDP. Human Development Report 1993; **Col 2:** World Resources 1994-95; **Col 3:** World Bank. World Developme Report 1993; UNICEF. The State of the World's Children, 1993; **Col 4:** American Automobile Manufacturers' Association; **Col 5:** World Resources 1994-95.

INTERNATIONAL TABLE

6 ted land rcentage tal land 89-90	7 Trade in live birds reported to CITES 1992		8 Commercial fertilizer use kgs per hectare of cropland 1991	9 Treaties as of mid-1993		
	imports	exports		1972 CITES Endangered species	1992 Climate Change Treaty	
2.9%	–	–	6	R (ratified)	S (signatory)	Afghanistan
8.2%	6	0	114	–	–	Albania
2.0%	1	0	15	R	R	Algeria
2.5%	0	2	4	–	S	Angola
1.7%	0	77,170	6	R	S	Argentina
–	–	–	39	–	R	Armenia
3.9%	0	39	26	R	R	Australia
8.7%	4,252	0	199	R	S	Austria
–	–	–	38	–	S	Azerbaijan
2.4%	61	0	–	–	–	Bahamas
5.9%	–	–	–	–	–	Bahrain
5.0%	25	0	101	R	S	Bangladesh
–	63	0	–	–	–	Barbados
–	–	–	234	–	S	Belarus
3.0%	91,484	0	470	R	S	Belgium
4.4%	0	6	89	R	S	Belize
1.8%	0	510	4	R	S	Benin
5.4%	–	–	–	–	S	Bhutan
1.3%	7	0	3	R	S	Bolivia
9.3%	0	1,974	1	R	S	Botswana
5.4%	494	0	54	R	S	Brazil
4.6%	–	–	–	–	–	Brunei
5.0%	4	0	153	R	S	Bulgaria
4.3%	0	0	6	R	R	Burkina Faso
2.6%	0	5	2	R	S	Burundi
5.8%	–	–	2	S	–	Cambodia
3.0%	0	18,194	3	R	S	Cameroon
8.8%	13,332	0	46	R	R	Canada
0.2%	0	1	0	R	S	Central African Rep.
7.5%	0	2	2	R	S	Chad
0.2%	247	0	69	R	S	Chile
1.8%	2	0	284	R	R	China
3.6%	0	12	104	R	S	Colombia
8.7%	–	–	–	–	–	Comoros
5.7%	0	45	6	R	S	Congo
2.0%	–	–	–	–	–	Cook Islands
2.1%	14	0	212	R	S	Costa Rica
24.0%	0	5,850	10	–	S	Côte d'Ivoire
–	–	–	–	–	–	Croatia
25.1%	0	405	158	R	S	Cuba
3.3%	–	–	–	–	–	Cyprus
–	–	–	–	R	R	Czech Republic
11.6%	9,060	0	243	R	S	Denmark

l 6: UNDP. *Human Development Report 1993; World Resources 1994-95;* **Col 7** and **8:** *World Resources 1994-95;* **Col 9:** *World Resources 1994-95* d 1992-93.

	1 Population 1995 millions	2 Percentage of total population which is urban 1995	3 Percentage of household income spent on food 1980-85	4 Number of cars 1991 thousands	5 CO₂ emissio from industi processes 1ⁿ thousand metric
Djibouti	0.5	82.8%	–	13.0	359
Dominica	0.1	–	–	4.7	–
Dominican Republic	7.9	64.6%	46%	139.1	6,262
Ecuador	11.8	60.6%	30%	–	17,785
Egypt	58.5	44.8%	49%	500.0	81,667
El Salvador	5.8	46.7%	33%	80.0	2,532
Equatorial Guinea	0.4	30.5%	–	5.5	121
Estonia	1.6	73.1%	–	–	–
Ethiopia	58.0	13.4%	49%	37.8	2,825
Fiji	0.8	40.7%	–	32.0	689
Finland	5.1	60.3%	16%	1,944.7	52,047
France	57.8	72.8%	16%	23,810.0	374,113
Gabon	1.4	50.0%	–	23.0	5,987
Gambia	1.0	25.5%	–	6.0	198
Georgia	5.5	–		–	–
Germany	81.3	86.5%	–	37,609.2	969,630
Ghana	17.5	36.3%	66%	82.0	3,455
Greece	10.3	65.0%	30%	1,777.5	72,866
Guatemala	10.6	41.5%	36%	145.0	4,074
Guinea	6.7	29.6%	–	14.0	1,026
Guinea Bissau	1.1	22.2%	–	3.3	205
Guyana	0.8	35.3%	–	–	850
Haiti	7.2	31.6%	–	33.0	733
Honduras	6.0	47.7%	39%	45.0	1,946
Hong Kong	5.8	–	12%	260.2	–
Hungary	10.5	67.7%	25%	2,015.5	63,574
Iceland	0.3	91.6%	–	120.9	1,803
India	931.0	26.8%	52%	2,490.8	703,550
Indonesia	201.5	32.5%	48%	1,416.2	170,468
Iran	66.7	60.4%	37%	1,600.0	222,361
Iraq	21.2	74.6%	–	650.0	520,281
Ireland	3.5	58.4%	22%	828.2	32,236
Israel	5.9	92.7%	21%	848.6	35,566
Italy	57.9	70.5%	19%	28,200.0	402,516
Jamaica	2.6	55.4%	36%	97.5	4,672
Japan	125.9	77.9%	17%	37,076.0	1,091,147
Jordan	4.8	71.5%	35%	172.1	10,010
Kazakhstan	17.4	–		–	–
Kenya	27.9	27.7%	38%	150.0	4,847
Kirgistan	4.7	–		–	–
Korea (North)	23.9	61.3%	–	–	243,235
Korea (South)	45.2	77.6%	35%	2,727.9	264,647
Kuwait	1.6	97.8%	–	500.0	11,842

Sources: Col 1: *World Resources 1994-95;* UNDP. *Human Development Report 1993;* **Col 2:** *World Resources 1994-95;* **Col 3:** World Bank. *World Developme Report 1993;* UNICEF. *The State of the World's Children, 1993;* **Col 4:** American Automobile Manufacturers' Association; **Col 5:** *World Resources 1994-95.*

6 sted land ercentage tal land 89-90	7 Trade in live birds reported to CITES 1992		8 Commercial fertilizer use kgs per hectare of cropland **1991**	9 Treaties as of mid-1993		
	imports	exports		1972 CITES Endangered species	1992 Climate Change Treaty	
0.3%	–	–	–	R	S	Djibouti
1.3%	–	–	–	–	–	Dominica
2.8%	78	0	60	R	S	Dominican Republic
0.5%	0	9	28	R	R	Ecuador
<1%	1,000	0	361	R	S	Egypt
5.0%	0	6	105	R	S	El Salvador
6.2%	–	–	0	–	–	Equatorial Guinea
–	–	–	–	R	S	Estonia
4.7%	–	–	7	R	S	Ethiopia
4.9%	–	–	83	–	R	Fiji
6.2%	0	1,012	174	R	S	Finland
6.9%	27,374	0	301	R	S	France
7.6%	0	29	2	R	S	Gabon
6.2%	–	–	7	R	S	Gambia
–	–	–	43	–	–	Georgia
9.7%	116,894	0	520	R	S	Germany
5.4%	0	6,015	4	R	S	Ghana
0.0%	681	0	172	R	S	Greece
5.3%	65	0	71	R	S	Guatemala
9.5%	0	121,887	2	R	R	Guinea
8.1%	0	1	3	R	S	Guinea Bissau
3.2%	0	18,399	30	R	S	Guyana
1.5%	0	2	3	–	S	Haiti
9.9%	0	2,463	14	R	S	Honduras
2.1%	–	–	–	–	–	Hong Kong
8.3%	474	0	142	R	S	Hungary
1.2%	8	0	–	–	R	Iceland
2.4%	0	31,470	73	R	R	India
2.6%	0	58,271	109	R	S	Indonesia
1.0%	–	–	77	R	S	Iran
4.3%	5	0	34	–	–	Iraq
4.9%	0	0	725	S	S	Ireland
5.4%	2,498	0	240	R	S	Israel
22.9%	20,542	0	160	R	S	Italy
7.2%	0	2	94	–	S	Jamaica
6.7%	12,172	0	402	R	R	Japan
0.8%	0	1	50	R	R	Jordan
–	–	–	3	–	S	Kazakhstan
4.1%	0	11	45	R	S	Kenya
–	–	–	18	–	–	Kirgistan
74.5%	10	0	409	–	S	Korea (North)
55.7%	1,929	0	440	R	S	Korea (South)
0.1%	5	0	133	S	–	Kuwait

l 6: UNDP. *Human Development Report 1993; World Resources 1994-95;* **Col 7** and **8:** *World Resources 1994-95;* **Col 9:** *World Resources 1994-95* d 1992-93.

	1 Population 1995 millions	2 Percentage of total population which is urban 1995	3 Percentage of household income spent on food 1980-85	4 Number of cars 1991 thousands	5 CO₂ emissi from industr processes 19 thousand metric
Laos	4.9	21.7%	–	8.5	253
Latvia	2.7	72.9%	–	–	–
Lebanon	3.0	87.2%	–	–	8,361
Lesotho	2.0	23.1%	–	–	–
Liberia	3.0	50.6%	–	–	275
Libya	5.4	86.0%	–	450.0	43,068
Lithuania	3.8	72.1%	–	–	–
Luxembourg	0.4	–	–	200.7	–
Madagascar	14.2	27.1%	59%	46.4	1,074
Malawi	11.3	13.5%	30%	17.0	630
Malaysia	20.1	47.2%	–	2,000.0	61,196
Mali	10.8	27.0%	57%	22.0	436
Malta	0.4	–	–	–	–
Mauritania	2.3	53.8%	–	10.0	2,704
Mauritius	1.1	40.7%	24%	50.0	1,216
Mexico	93.7	75.3%	35%	7,400.0	339,873
Moldova	4.4	–	–	–	–
Mongolia	2.5	60.9%	–	–	9,823
Morocco	28.3	48.4%	38%	719.2	24,197
Mozambique	16.4	34.3%	–	88.0	1,030
Myanmar	46.6	26.2%	–	35.0	4,961
Namibia	1.7	30.9%	–	–	–
Nepal	22.1	13.7%	57%	–	923
Netherlands	15.5	88.9%	13%	5,569.1	138,990
New Zealand	3.6	84.3%	12%	1,554.5	23,842
Nicaragua	4.4	62.9%	–	35.0	2,074
Niger	9.1	23.1%	–	18.0	1,030
Nigeria	126.9	39.3%	48%	785.0	91,930
Norway	4.4	77.0%	15%	1,614.6	58,672
Oman	1.8	13.2%	–	145.0	11,695
Pakistan	135.0	34.7%	37%	721.2	68,487
Panama	2.7	54.9%	38%	150.0	3,594
Papua New Guinea	4.3	17.8%	–	–	2,257
Paraguay	4.9	50.7%	30%	–	1,781
Peru	23.9	72.2%	35%	399.9	19,155
Philippines	69.3	45.7%	51%	456.6	44,587
Poland	38.7	63.9%	29%	6,112.2	308,164
Portugal	9.9	36.4%	34%	1,800.0	41,792
Quatar	.4	–	–	115.2	–
Romania	23.5	56.2%	–	–	138,027
Russia	149.7	–	–	17,000.0	–
Rwanda	8.3	6.1%	29%	15.0	436
St. Lucia	0.1	–	–	7.0	–

Sources: Col 1: *World Resources 1994-95;* UNDP. *Human Development Report 1993;* **Col 2:** *World Resources 1994-95;* **Col 3:** World Bank. *World Developme Report 1993;* UNICEF. *The State of the World's Children,* 1993; **Col. 4:** American Automobile Manufacturers' Association; **Col. 5:** *World Resources 1994-95.*

INTERNATIONAL TABLE

6 rested land percentage total land 1989-90	7 Trade in live birds reported to CITES 1992		8 Commercial fertilizer use kgs per hectare of cropland 1991	9 Treaties as of mid-1993		
	imports	exports		1972 CITES Endangered species	1992 Climate Change Treaty	
55.5%	–	–	2	–	–	Laos
45.1%	–	–	151	–	S	Latvia
7.8%	2	0	93	–	S	Lebanon
65.9%	–	–	16	S	S	Lesotho
18.3%	0	2,939	3	R	S	Liberia
0.4%	20	0	37	–	S	Libya
–	–	–	–	–	S	Lithuania
–	–	–	–	R	–	Luxembourg
27.0%	0	1,923	3	R	S	Madagascar
39.8%	–	–	36	R	S	Malawi
58.1%	0	2,030	188	R	S	Malaysia
5.7%	0	89,033	8	–	S	Mali
–	31	0	–	–	–	Malta
4.8%	–	–	10	–	S	Mauritania
30.8%	76	0	277	R	S	Mauritius
22.5%	498	0	69	R	R	Mexico
–	–	–	122	–	S	Moldova
8.9%	–	–	12	–	R	Mongolia
17.8%	0	37	35	R	S	Morocco
18.3%	0	21,322	1	R	S	Mozambique
49.3%	0	1,298	7	–	S	Myanmar
22.0%	53	0	0	R	S	Namibia
18.1%	–	–	27	R	S	Nepal
8.8%	186,749	0	614	R	S	Netherlands
27.3%	0	244	899	R	R	New Zealand
29.4%	0	6,899	29	R	S	Nicaragua
1.6%	46	0	1	R	S	Niger
13.4%	0	15	12	R	S	Nigeria
27.1%	62	0	234	R	R	Norway
0.0%	11	0	122	–	S	Oman
4.5%	0	53	89	R	S	Pakistan
44.0%	0	47	50	R	S	Panama
84.4%	–	–	33	R	R	Papua New Guinea
36.1%	–	–	9	R	S	Paraguay
53.6%	0	23,737	32	R	R	Peru
35.4%	545	0	65	R	S	Philippines
28.7%	0	968	138	R	S	Poland
32.3%	62,165	0	84	R	S	Portugal
–	–	–	–	–	–	Quatar
27.7%	–	–	98	–	S	Romania
–	–	–	52	R	S	Russia
22.6%	–	–	2	R	S	Rwanda
13.1%	–	–	–	–	–	St. Lucia

Col 6: UNDP. *Human Development Report 1993; World Resources 1994-95;* **Col 7** and **8:** *World Resources 1994-95;* **Col 9:** *World Resources 1994-95*
nd 1992-93.

	1 Population 1995 millions	2 Percentage of total population which is urban 1995	3 Percentage of household income spent on food 1980-85	4 Number of cars 1991 thousands	5 CO$_2$ emission from industri processes 19 thousand metric
Saõ Tome & Principe	0.1	–	–	–	–
St. Vincent & Grenadines	0.1	–	–	4.5	–
Saudi Arabia	17.6	80.2%	–	2,300.0	214,919
Senegal	8.4	42.3%	49%	97.0	2,799
Seychelles	<0.1	–	–	4.7	–
Sierra Leone	4.7	36.2%	56%	35.9	689
Singapore	2.85	100%	19%	285.3	41,293
Slovak Republic	5.3	–	–	–	–
Solomon Islands	0.4	17.1%	–	–	161
Somalia	10.2	25.8%	–	10.5	524
South Africa	42.7	50.8%	34%	3,461.4	278,695
Spain	39.3	80.7%	24%	12,537.1	219,877
Sri Lanka	18.4	22.4%	43%	180.1	4,166
Sudan	29.0	24.6%	60%	116.0	3,404
Suriname	0.5	50.4%	–	35.0	2,019
Swaziland	0.9	31.2%	–	21.3	330
Sweden	8.8	84.7%	13%	3,619.4	53,498
Switzerland	7.0	64.0%	–	3,065.8	41,843
Syria	14.8	52.4%	–	119.0	29,766
Tajikistan	6.0	–	–	–	–
Taiwan	20.6	–	–	2,000.0	–
Tanzania	30.7	24.4%	64%	46.6	2,158
Thailand	58.3	35.4%	30%	825.1	100,896
Togo	4.1	30.8%	–	26.0	722
Trinidad & Tobago	1.3	66.6%	19%	–	18,430
Tunisia	8.9	59.0%	37%	330.0	14,810
Turkey	62.0	68.8%	40%	1,864.3	142,555
Turkmenistan	4.2	–	–	–	–
Uganda	20.4	12.5%	–	–	912
Ukraine	52.4	–	–	–	–
United Arab Emirates	1.8	84.0%	–	300.0	59,459
United Kingdom	58.1	89.5%	12%	22,744.1	577,157
United States	263.1	76.2%	10%	142,955.6	4,931,630
Uruguay	3.2	90.3%	31%	200.0	4,459
Uzbekistan	22.8	–	–	–	–
Vanuatu	0.2	–	–	–	–
Venezuela	21.5	92.9%	23%	1,590.0	121,604
Vietnam	73.8	20.8%	–	–	20,573
Yemen	13.9	33.6%	–	165.4	9,940
Yugoslavia	24.1	60.7%	–	3,600.0	87,225
Zaire	43.8	29.1%	55%	100.0	4,236
Zambia	9.4	43.1%	36%	100.0	2,429
Zimbabwe	11.5	32.1%	40%	200.0	16,983

Sources: Col 1: *World Resources 1994-95*; UNDP. *Human Development Report 1993*; **Col 2:** *World Resources 1994-95*; **Col 3:** World Bank. *World Developmen Report 1993*; UNICEF. *The State of the World's Children*, 1993; **Col. 4:** American Automobile Manufacturers' Association; **Col. 5:** *World Resources 1994-95*.

INTERNATIONAL TABLE

6 ested land percentage total land 1989-90	7 Trade in live birds reported to CITES 1992		8 Commercial fertilizer use kgs per hectare of cropland 1991	9 Treaties as of mid-1993		
	imports	exports		1972 CITES Endangered species	1992 Climate Change Treaty	
–	–	–	–	–	–	Saõ Tome & Principe
35.9%	–	–	–	–	–	St. Vincent & Grenadines
0.6%	947	0	208	–	–	Saudi Arabia
30.9%	0	270,671	6	R	S	Senegal
18.5%	–	–	–	–	–	Seychelles
28.9%	0	4,019	2	–	S	Sierra Leone
4.9%	5,399	0	–	–	S	Singapore
–	–	–	–	R	S	Slovak Republic
91.5%	0	127	0	–	S	Solomon Islands
14.5%	0	1	2	R	–	Somalia
3.7%	7,751	0	59	R	S	South Africa
31.3%	40,736	0	98	R	S	Spain
27.0%	32	0	98	R	S	Sri Lanka
19.0%	37	0	6	R	S	Sudan
95.2%	0	8,597	20	R	S	Suriname
6.3%	–	–	60	–	S	Swaziland
68.1%	4,022	0	113	R	R	Sweden
26.5%	3,854	0	413	R	S	Switzerland
3.9%	–	–	51	–	–	Syria
–	–	–	50	–	–	Tajikistan
–	–	–	–	–	–	Taiwan
46.3%	0	122,761	15	R	S	Tanzania
27.9%	234	0	39	R	S	Thailand
29.6%	0	4,643	15	R	S	Togo
43.1%	236	0	67	R	S	Trinidad & Tobago
4.1%	1	0	20	R	R	Tunisia
26.2%	898	0	65	–	–	Turkey
–	–	–	7	–	–	Turkmenistan
28.1%	–	–	0	R	R	Uganda
–	–	–	126	–	S	Ukraine
<1.0%	2,612	0	359	R	–	United Arab Emirates
9.8%	121,364	0	350	R	S	United Kingdom
32.1%	154,951	0	99	R	R	United States
3.8%	0	25,040	57	R	S	Uruguay
–	–	–	41	–	R	Uzbekistan
75.0%	0	15	–	–	–	Vanuatu
34.5%	0	6	116	R	S	Venezuela
30.1%	0	900	96	S	S	Vietnam
7.7%	1	1	–	–	S	Yemen
–	2,497	0	99	–	S	Yugoslavia
77.0%	0	711	1	R	S	Zaire
38.9%	0	1	13	R	R	Zambia
49.7%	0	1,156	56	R	R	Zimbabwe

Col 6: UNDP. *Human Development Report 1993; World Resources 1994-95;* **Col 7** and **8:** *World Resources 1994-95;* **Col 9:** *World Resources 1994-95 and 1992-93.*

MAJOR SOURCES

Brown, Lester. ed. *State of the World*. New York: Norton, 1992 and 1993.

Brown, Lester. ed. *Vital Signs 1993*. New York: Norton, 1993.

Buzzworm. ed. *1993 Earth Journal*. Boulder, CO: Buzzworm Books, 1992.

Crump, Andy. *Dictionary of Environment and Development*. London: Earthscan, 1991.

Gleick, Peter. ed. *Water in Crisis: A Guide to the World's Fresh Water Resources*. Oxford and New York: Oxford University Press, 1993.

Goldsmith, Edward and Nicholas Hildyard. *The Earth Report*. London: Price Sloan, 1988.

Lean, Geoffrey and Don Hinrichsen. *Atlas of the Environment*. Oxford: Helicon, 1992.

Myers, Norman. *Gaia: An Atlas of Planet Management*. revised ed. New York: Doubleday, 1993.

Organisation for Economic Cooperation and Development (OECD). *OECD Environmental Data Compendium 1993*. Paris: OECD, 1993.

United Nations. *Statistical Yearbook 1990-91*. New York: UN, 1993.

United Nations Development Programme. *Human Development Report 1993*. Oxford and New York: Oxford University Press, 1993.

United Nations Environment Programme. *Environmental Data Report, 1991-92*. Washington D.C. and London: UNEP, 1992.

UNICEF. *The State of the World's Children 1993*. Oxford and New York: Oxford University Press, 1993.

World Bank. *World Development Report 1993*. Oxford and New York: Oxford University Press, 1993.

World Resources Institute. *The 1994 Information Please Environmental Almanac*. New York: Houghton Mifflin; London: Cassell, 1994.

World Resources Institute. *World Resources 1992-93*. Oxford and New York: Oxford University Press, 1992.

World Resources Institute. *World Resources 1994-95*. Oxford and New York: Oxford University Press, 1994.

NOTES

1 TO HAVE – AND HAVE NOT

In 1983, the United Nations convened an independent taskforce, the World Commission on Environment and Development, to examine the global environment crisis. Four years later, the Commission published *Our Common Future*, an influential report which unequivocally identified poverty "as a major cause and effect of global environmental problems." The report affirmed that the gap between rich and poor was widening, and concluded that there was "little prospect, given present trends and institutional arrangements, that this process will be reversed." For the environment, this was a grim prognosis.

Poverty pushes people (and states) into a short-term, often reckless, use of resources and puts pressures on ecosystems that poor governments cannot afford to alleviate. Such environmental pressures of poverty are typically manifested most acutely on a local scale so it is the same poor population which most directly suffers the consequences of degradation. As increasing degradation encourages ever more desperate exploitation of available resources, environmental quality and poverty become locked together in a deadly relationship.

At the other end of the scale, wealthier people (and states) consume more than their fair share of the world's resources and produce disproportionate shares of pollution and environmental disruption, much of which reverberates through global ecosystems. The gap between rich and poor creates yet another set of environmental pressures: the poor aspire to achieve the same unsustainable levels of consumption as the wealthy, and the wealthy attempt to protect their privileges.

The Human Development Index (HDI) shown on this map is an international measure developed by the United Nations. The index combines information on life expectancy, educational attainment and income; each country's "score" is tallied and can then be ranked in comparison to other countries. The development indicators that comprise the HDI give a much broader measurement of "well-being" than do many of the more conventional global rankings which are based on narrow economic indicators such as Gross National Profit (GNP).

Sources:
United Nations Development Programme. *Human Development Report 1993*. New York: Oxford University Press,1993; World Commission on Environment and Development. *Our Common Future*. New York: Oxford University Press, 1987; press reports.

2 HUNGER

Each year there are more people in the world who do not get enough to eat. *The Hunger Report*, an annual assessment of the state of hunger in the world, introduces the topic in this way: "No one really knows how many hungry people there are in the world. No one knows the toll of hunger because hunger is difficult to define, because the statistical data are weak or nonexistent, and because efforts to improve data collection and analysis have been limited. But beyond these real difficulties, we may not know how many hungry people there are in the world because we may not want to know. To know how many hungry there are in a world of plenty is to measure the inadequacies of our economies to sustain all, of our societies to provide for all, and of our common humanity to care for all."

The causes of hunger are complex, but as the United Nations Development Programme's

Human Development Report has asserted, the primary cause of hunger is poverty; countries and families that can afford food have little problem acquiring all they want, even under conditions of general scarcity. There is a sharp divide between glut for the rich and hunger for the poor. On average, people in the richest countries eat 30 to 40 percent more calories than they need. (The World Health Organization considers that 2,500 calories per day meets basic needs.) There is also, of course, a sharp divide within countries, where in many cases the top fifth of the population is ten to 20 times more affluent than the bottom fifth.

Most international statistics on food and hunger measure the average availability of food supply, which is not the same as food consumption: just because food is "available" does not mean that everyone has equal access to it. Food consumption is mediated by class, gender, and age, among other variables. In many poor countries, households spend a significant portion of their income on food. In the early 1980s, the period for which data is available, the average expenditure on food in Tanzania, for example, was 64 percent of household income; in the Philippines, 51 percent; in Egypt, 49 percent; in Kenya 38 percent. In richer industrialized states, expenditures for food range on average between ten to 20 percent of household income.

The link between food being available and food being consumed is often tenuous, and is particularly subject to disruptions, most noticeably by war. Food supplies are often intentional targets in times of armed conflict. And when food supplies are disrupted, the first to suffer are the poorest, hungriest and most vulnerable members of the population — chief among whom are women and their dependent children.

On a global basis, food production continues to rise. But almost two-thirds of poor countries faced stagnant or declining levels of per capita food production in the early 1990s. In Africa, absolute production has increased, but on a per capita basis food production has steadily fallen, and the continent as a whole is more hungry in the mid-1990s than it was in the 1960s. As food production has fallen, food imports have increased; the demand for imports and the inability to pay for them will worsen over the coming decades. It is a terrible irony that many countries where hunger is prevalent are net exporters of food. In most poor countries, increasing shares of land are being devoted to export-crop production, often even in the midst of famine.

The production and supply of food are inextricably tied to the state of the environment. The problems which will affect the availability of food include accelerating land erosion, increasing agro-chemical dependence, the need to conserve wild genes for the protection and maintenance of crops, and even the possibility of a changing world climate.

Sources:

Food and Agriculture Organization (FAO). *The State of Food and Agriculture 1993*. Rome: FAO, 1993; Food and Agriculture Organization (FAO). *Trade Yearbook 1992*. Rome: FAO, 1993; International Development Research Centre. *Our Common Bowl: Global Food Interdependence*. Ottawa, 1992; Jenkins, Robin. *Bringing Rio Home: Biodiversity in Our Food and Farming*. London: SAFE, 1992; Kates, Robert et al. *The Hunger Report: 1988 and Update*. Brown University: Alan Shawn Feinstein World Hunger Program, 1989; United Nations Development Programme (UNDP). *Human Development Report 1993*. New York: Oxford University Press, 1993; UNICEF. *The State of the World's Children 1993*. New York: Oxford University Press, 1993; World Resources Institute. *World Resources 1994-95*. New York: Oxford University Press, 1994; World Bank. *World Development Report 1993*. New York:Oxford University Press, 1993.

3 THE FATTED CALF

Most people in the world live on a substantially vegetarian diet. Meat-eating is a habit largely peculiar to the affluent West. But many poor countries are trying to emulate Western culture and, associated as it is with "development," meat-eating is increasing worldwide. In virtually every country, rising income levels over the past 50 years have gone hand in hand with increased meat consumption. In Jamaica, for example, beef is now the main source of protein for the wealthiest 25 percent of the population; for the poorest 25 percent of the population, wheat flour is the number one source of protein, while beef ranks thirteenth. In Madagascar, the wealthiest families consume 12 times as much animal protein as the poorest families. There is also a connection between masculinity and meat-eating: where meat is scarce or highly valued, meat-eating is typically considered to be a prerogative of men.

In environmental terms, meat-eating is a costly habit. The world's livestock herds consume increasing quantities of land, energy, and water. A quarter of the earth's landmass is used as pasture for cattle and other livestock; more than half the farmland in the U.S.A. is devoted to beef production. While it takes, on average, 25 gallons (113 litres) of water to produce a pound of wheat in modern Western farming systems, it requires an astounding 2,500 gallons (11,250 litres) of water to produce a pound of meat. Throughout the world, livestock herds accelerate erosion and desertification; 85 percent of topsoil loss in the U.S.A. is directly attributed to livestock ranching, for example.

Some of these costs are borne only by meat-eaters and meat-eating cultures but many other associated costs ripple across the globe. For example, the spread of beef production is a major contributor to deforestation in Central and South America. In Mexico alone, 37 million acres of forest have been destroyed since 1987 to provide grazing land for cattle. Between 1966 and 1983, 40,000 square miles of Brazilian Amazon forest were cleared for commercial development, almost 40 percent of which was cleared for large-scale cattle ranching.

Meat eating significantly affects global food production, contributing to food scarcity for many and glut for the few. There has been a fundamental shift in world agriculture this century from food grains to feed grains, and cattle now compete with people for food. A third of the world's fish catch and more than a third of the world's total grain output is fed to livestock. In the U.S.A., the world's premiere meat-eating country, 80 percent of the corn grown and 95 percent of the oats grown are fed to livestock. On average, over 70 percent of grain produced in the U.S.A. is fed to livestock.

Cattle are inefficient converters of food, however. In cycling our grain through livestock, we waste 90 percent of its protein and 96 percent of its calories. An acre of cereal can produce five times more protein than an acre devoted to meat production; and legumes (beans, lentils, peas) can produce ten times as much. Thus the greater the human consumption of animal products, the fewer people can be fed.

Sources:

Buzzworm. *1993 Earth Journal.* Boulder, CO: Buzzworm, 1992; Brown, Lester. ed. *Vital Signs 1993.* New York: Norton, 1993; Brown, Lester. ed. *State of the World 1992.* New York: Norton, 1992; Food and Agriculture Organization (FAO). *Socio-Economic Aspects of Sustainable Development.* Rome: FAO, 1992; Goldsmith, Edward and Nicholas Hildyard. eds. *The Earth Report.* London: Price Stern, 1988; Global Tomorrow Coalition. *Global Ecology Handbook.* Boston: Beacon Press, 1990; Myers, Norman. ed. *Gaia: An Atlas of Planet Management.* revised ed. New York: Doubleday, 1993; Organization for Economic Cooperation and Development (OECD). *Meat Balances in the OECD 1984-1990.* Paris: OECD, 1992; Pimentel, David and Carl Hall. *Food and Natural Resources.* San Diego, CA: Academic Press, 1989; Rifkin, Jeremy. *Beyond Beef.* New York: Plume Publishing, 1992; Robbins, John. *A Diet for a New America.* Walpole, NH: Stillpoint, 1987; World Resources Institute. *World Resources 1992-93.* New York: Oxford University Press, 1992.

4 DRINKING WATER

Every day, at least 25,000 people in the world die from illnesses caused by unsafe water — and everywhere in the world, rivers and lakes which supply drinking water are also used as sewage and industrial waste dumps.

In general, the availability of safe water is linked to economic status. In most industrialized countries, water quality has improved over the last 20 years, mainly due to increased sewage treatment. In developing countries, especially around urban areas, water quality is generally deteriorating. Approximately half the population in the Third World is still without safe drinking water despite the progress made between 1980 and 1990, during the United Nations Decade on Drinking Water Supply.

In poor countries, the greatest difficulties in providing safe water are the cost of bringing piped water to more people, and the logistical problems of protecting water supplies from sewage pollution. Throughout the developing world, most sewage is discharged into surface waters without any treatment. For example, out of some 3,119 towns and cities in India, only 217 have partial or complete sewage treatment facilities. Of 78 rivers monitored in China, 54 are categorized as "seriously polluted" with untreated sewage and industrial wastes. More than 40 of Malaysia's major rivers are so polluted that they are said to be biologically dead.

In the rich world, the biggest threats to water safety are from industrial and chemical pollution, especially agricultural chemical runoff. Even with stringent water quality standards, 38 percent of the rivers in the U.S.A. are classified as too polluted to swim in let alone to drink. In Poland, the Vistula River is so polluted that along most of its length its waters are unsuitable even for industrial use.

Ideally, drinking water should come from unpolluted groundwater. However, this is an ideal in rapid retreat. Currently more than half the population of OECD countries and more than 70 percent of the population of the U.S.A. drinks water that has been passed through waste water treatment plants. The danger of treated waste water is that not all the impurities may be removed; additionally, the chemical agents used in treatment may themselves pose health risks. Throughout the early 1990s, in some OECD countries, there were frequent reports of contaminated drinking water.

There are big differences around the world in water use. Rich countries are profligate water users. While more than half the world's population must make do with less than 25 gallons (113 litres) a day each for domestic use, water use in the U.S.A. averages about 159 gallons (716 litres) per person per day. Everywhere, demands on water supplies are high and growing fast. In the U.S.A., for example, it is estimated that household water consumption will quadruple between 1967 and 2000, while demands made by industry will increase fivefold. Without powerful conservation measures, American consumption may exceed 260 gallons (1,170 litres) per person per day by the year 2000.

The World Health Organization (WHO) defines reasonable access to safe drinking water in an urban area as "access to piped water or a public standpipe within 200 metres of a dwelling;" for rural areas, WHO defines reasonable access as "drinking water within 15 minutes walking distance." These definitions, even down to what is rural and what is urban, are clearly open to different interpretations and comparisons between countries may be misleading. In general, much of the international data available on water provision must be accepted with skepticism.

Sources:
International Bottled Water Association. Alexandria, VA, USA; Organisation for Economic Cooperation and Development (OECD). *OECD Environmental Data Compendium 1993.* Paris: OECD, 1993; United Nations. *Statistical Yearbook. 1990-91.* New York: UN, 1993; World Health Organization (WHO). *World Health Statistics Annual 1991.* New York: WHO, 1991; World Resources Institute. *The 1994 Information Please Environmental Almanac.* New York: Houghton Mifflin, 1994.

5 WATER RESOURCES

Fresh water may be a renewable resource but it is not finite. Less than three percent of the world's water is fresh, and most of that is frozen at the North and South poles. Only about one-hundredth of a percent of the world's total water is easily available: if all the earth's water could be contained in a gallon jug, the available fresh water would equal just over a tablespoonful.

Demand for water has dramatically increased. Global per capita water use is nearly 50 percent higher today than it was in 1950; by the year 2000, global consumption will be ten times greater than it was in 1900. The increasing consumption is only partly a result of growing human numbers – demand for water has been growing much faster than the population. Worldwide, irrigation consumes the largest single share of water. Increases in affluence, "development," and improved living standards have put even greater strains on water supplies. And the climate changes predicted to occur as a consequence of global warming will almost certainly aggravate existing water imbalances and increase the shortages.

Twenty-six countries, collectively home to 232 million people, already face conditions of water scarcity. The Middle East is the most concentrated region of scarcity; observers predict that water — not oil — will be at the center of any future Middle East wars.

Water serves many roles: it is a service commodity for agriculture, industry, and urban growth, but it is also a key life-support for all species and ecosystems. Ecosystems are generally losing out in this conflict. A long list of natural areas and unique wild places destroyed or at grave risk from increased rates of water extraction includes the Florida Everglades and California's Mono Lake in the U.S.A., the Donana wetlands in Spain, the Sudd swamps in the Sudan, the Okavango Basin in Botswana, and the Aral Sea, now divided between Kazakhstan and Uzbekistan.

Sources:
Brown, Lester. ed. *Vital Signs 1993*. New York: Norton, 1993; Gleick, Peter. ed. *Water in Crisis: A Guide to the World's Fresh Water Resources*. New York: Oxford University Press, 1993; Gleick, Peter. *Water in Crisis*. Occasional Paper Series. *Environmental Change and Acute Conflict*. 1 (September 1992); Myers, Norman. *Gaia: An Atlas of Planet Management*. revised ed. New York: Doubleday, 1993; National Geographic Society. *Water*. Special edition. November 1993. Postel, Sandra. "Facing Water Scarcity" in Lester Brown. ed. *State of the World 1993*. New York: Norton, 1993; United Nations Environment Programme (UNEP). *Environmental Data Report, 1991-92*. Oxford, UK and Cambridge, MA: Basil Blackwell, 1992; World Resources Institute. *The 1994 Information Please Environmental Almanac*. New York: Houghton Mifflin, 1994.

6 A POPULAR PLANET

Population growth rates are going down in most parts of the world, but the world's population will continue to grow, pushed upwards by the sheer momentum of its numbers.

The world's population now grows by about 90 million people a year. Some would argue, including many environmentalists, that there is a direct correlation between population growth and the world's increasing environmental problems. The evidence does not bear this out, however. While population growth is now a Third World phenomenon, the large-scale global environmental crises we face are largely the product of the voracious resource appetites of industrial economies and lifestyles. In calculating how much we burden the atmosphere, one economist estimates that the "cost" of one U.S. citizen is 16 times that of a Third World citizen; and the "cost" of a person in Western Europe is five times that of someone in the developing world. The average person in the industrial world consumes ten times as much energy, ten times as much steel, 15 times as much paper, and one-and-a-half times as much food as does the average person living in the Third World. The most pressing global environmental problems — such as fossil fuel pollution (and the related threat of global warming), the use and production of ozone-depleting chemicals, acid rain emissions, production of household waste, municipal waste, and toxic industrial waste, the luxury trade in exotic animal and bird species, and the stripping of the world's forests — are not so much caused by the "excessive" number of people in poor countries as by the excessive pressures that the richer countries exert on the world's biosphere.

This is not to deny that growing numbers of people burden natural ecosystems; they do. Destruction of wildlife habitats, forest cutback for subsistence agriculture, and deterioration of urban water quality, for example, stem in some measure from the sheer pressure of human need. The environmental impacts of a growing population are then magnified by growing affluence, industrialization and increasing consumption.

In turn, in a world of social inequities, environmental problems themselves encourage high rates of population growth — in countries where infants die regularly from gastro-intestinal disease brought on by lack of clean water, for example, women have to bear higher numbers of children to meet perceived population replacement levels. Population growth may well be a "problem," but not in the ways that most of us are encouraged to believe. And the solution to environmental problems is not simply, or even primarily, through population controls.

The world's population is urbanizing much faster than it is growing. Throughout the Third World, massive rural to urban shifts in population are occurring at breakneck pace. Many of these new urban arrivals are reluctant migrants, people displaced from rural areas by war, famine, massive "development" schemes, or agricultural "modernization." For others, the attractions of the city are not diminished by the reality of urban poverty: cities still offer the possibility of economic opportunities not found elsewhere, the hope of greater political or religious freedom, and amenities not available in rural settings.

The locus of global urbanization is shifting. In 1960, six of the largest ten cities were in industrialized countries: New York, Los Angeles, London, the Rhine/Ruhr conglomeration, Paris, and Moscow. By the year 2000, only two cities in the industrial world, New York and Tokyo, will remain in the top ten ranking. Mexico City, which will be the world's largest city by the year 2000, was ranked number 15 in size in 1960.

As cities grow, both in absolute size and proportional importance, they play a larger part in shaping the global environment. Under the pressure of urban sprawl, agricultural land is paved over, wetlands are drained, natural habitats are destroyed, rivers are diverted, and wildlife habitats are pushed further and further into the margins. The internal ecology of cities also changes: pollutants of all kinds are concentrated in urban centers, and many cities have become hazardous places in which to live. City residents also typically consume more industrial goods and energy-intensive services than their rural counterparts; they create more waste and more air and water pollution.

Sources:
Population Reference Bureau. *World Population Data Sheet 1993*. Washington D.C., 1993; United Nations. *Statistical Yearbook 1990-91*. New York: UN, 1993; World Resources Institute. *The 1994 Information Please Environmental Almanac*. New York: Houghton Mifflin, 1994; World Resources Institute. *World Resources 1994-95*. New York: Oxford University Press, 1994.

7 WASTE

It is extremely difficult to measure accurately levels of municipal and household waste, and, as most experts agree, the international information available is little more than an educated guess. However, some general points are clear: worldwide generation of municipal and household waste appears to amount to about one billion metric tons per year, and is growing rapidly; the biggest waste producers are rich countries, and, within poor countries, richer people. The U.S.A. alone generates an estimated 19 percent of the world's total domestic waste, and Japan another 4.4 percent. Affluence produces effluence, literally.

There are also significant differences in the kind of garbage thrown away by the rich and poor: in rich countries and communities, glass, paper, plastics, metals and other durable waste constitute a larger share of garbage than in poor countries, where more of the waste is organic material. This difference has important implications for waste disposal: organic garbage can be composted, which is the safest and cheapest method. The disposal of other materials is less easy and altogether more costly.

Most garbage, in most places in the world, is dumped in waste pits or landfills. But countries and cities everywhere are running out of space for landfills or, increasingly, closing existing ones because of environmental concerns. Incineration is one alternative but it is a dubious solution. It perpetuates a cycle of dependence on high-cost technological remedies for what are, essentially, social problems; moreover, it creates a toxic residue that in turn needs disposal. A 1994 legal ruling in the U.S.A. determined that incinerator ash must be classified as hazardous waste that cannot be dumped in ordinary landfills.

Recycling is a cheap, revenue-generating, and low-technology solution to the problem of waste disposal. It is gaining favor in most industrialized countries, although, ironically, recycling rates in the 1990s are still much lower than they were in the first half of the century. Germany has developed the most ambitious household waste recycling mandate in the world, requiring residents and industries to recycle or reuse everything related to the shipping and packaging of goods. In poor countries, recycling has always ranked high in waste reduction, and whole communities of people in most Third World cities support themselves as dump-scavengers and recyclers.

Some countries still dump their municipal garbage at sea. Although this practice is being phased out, we will live with its legacy for years to come: increasing epidemics of marine mammal illnesses and incidents of deep-sea trash washing up on beaches are already attracting attention in Western Europe and the U.S.A.

The disposal crisis has created an active international trade in waste. With no room in their own backyards, states and industries in the developed world are scanning the globe for countries poor enough to want to accept municipal trash for (usually low) dumping fees. Although many poor countries are increasingly reluctant to take trash for landfilling, there is a growing interest in shipping wastes to the Third World for "recycling."

Sources:

Darnay, Arsen. ed. *Statistical Record of the Environment.* Detroit, MI: Gale Research, 1992; *The Economist.* "A Survey of Waste and the Environment." special report. 29 May 1993; Gale Environmental Library. *Recycling Sourcebook.* Detroit, MI: Gale Research, 1993; Organisation for Economic Cooperation and Development (OECD). *OECD Environmental Data Compendium 1993.* Paris: OECD, 1993; United Nations Environment Programme (UNEP). *Environmental Data Report, 1991-92.* Washington D.C. and London: UNEP, 1992; World Resources Institute. *The 1994 Information Please Environmental Almanac.* New York: Houghton Mifflin, 1994.

8 ILL WIND

Measuring air quality is a precise science that must, by its nature, be carried out under imprecise and unpredictable conditions. Standardized international measurements are only available for a scattering of cities, and drawing comparisons among city data is difficult because of the wide variations in the circumstances of where, and when, and the frequency with which air monitoring samples are taken. Also, there is often a bias toward monitoring cities where there is already known to be an air quality problem. But despite these caveats, it is still possible to make certain generalizations about urban air quality. Worldwide, air pollution has been worsening, exacerbated by four particular factors: the expansion of cities; the increasing number of cars; rapid economic development; and increasing levels of energy consumption. Much of the world's population lives in cities where pollution levels frequently exceed those recommended World Health Organization. Recent and stringent air quality standards enacted in many of the world's richest countries are resulting in a small but noticeable improvement in air quality in some cities. The introduction of unleaded gasoline for cars has reduced lead pollution in many cities around the world.

The main map depicts urban levels of three air pollutants — sulphur dioxide, nitrogen dioxide, and particulates ("dust and dirt"). Ninety percent of anthropogenic sulphur dioxide emissions are from the burning of fossil fuels; nitrogen oxides come primarily from car and truck emissions; and particulates from both cars and fossil fuel combustion. All three contribute to a range of respiratory illnesses, including bronchitis, pneumonia, asthma, and lung cancer, although the health effects vary with the intensity and duration of exposures. Both sulphur and nitrogen dioxide are major components of acid rain, and nitrogen oxides further contribute to the greenhouse effect. Benzopyrene, a carcinogenic substance found in coal tar, is a significant pollutant in many Russian industrial cities. In the early 1990s, the Ministry of Health in Russia concluded that there were air pollution problems in all the major cities of the new states of former USSR; in many cities, pollution exceeded recommended health levels by more than 50 times.

The air in most of the world's cities is a chemical soup of dozens of pollutants, many more than are depicted on the main map. Other prevalent pollutants, for which there is no comparable global data, include carbon monoxide, largely the product of car emissions, and ozone, also known as "photochemical smog." Los Angeles has the greatest ozone problem in the world, because of its special topography and high density of cars, but photochemical pollution is now known to occur in and downwind of most major cities in the world. Eastern Europe, as a whole, suffers the worst air quality in the industrialized world.

Sources:

Buzzworm. ed. *1993 Earth Journal.* Boulder, CO: Buzzworm Books,1992; Elsom, Derek. *Atmospheric Pollution: A Global Problem.* second edition. Oxford and Cambridge, MA: Blackwell, 1993; Feshbach, Murray and Alfred Friendly Jr. *Ecocide in the USSR.* New York: Basic Books, 1992; Global Environment Monitoring System (GEMS). *Assessment of Air Quality.* Nairobi: UNEP/WHO,1988; Peterson, D.J. *Troubled Lands: The Legacy of Soviet Environmental Destruction.* Boulder,CO: Westview Press/RAND Research,1993; UNEP/WHO. *Urban Air Pollution in Megacities of the World.* Oxford: Basil Blackwell, 1992; World Resources Institute.*World Resources 1990-91.* New York: Oxford University Press, 1990; World Resources Institute. *The 1994 Information Please Environmental Almanac.* New York: Houghton Mifflin, 1994.

9 THE TRIUMPH OF THE CAR

Most of the world's people still rely on bicycles, public buses and trains, animal-drawn carts, and their own feet for transportation. In China, for example, there are currently 250 bicycles for every car, and, worldwide, bicycles outnumber cars by two to one. But the global trend is clearly towards the dominance of automobile-centered transportation systems.

The costs of car culture are high. Private automobiles clog the streets of most world cities, often bringing urban services to a standstill; expanding road networks consume scarce space, destroy wildlife habitat, and degrade both natural ecosystems and agricultural land; the fuel demands of private transport are depleting fossil fuel resources at an alarming rate. Worldwide, at least a third of an average city's land is devoted to roads, parking lots, and other car-related infrastructures.

Cars are the largest single source of air pollutants. In OECD countries, for example, on average 75 percent of carbon monoxide emissions, 48 percent of nitrogen oxides, and 13 percent of atmospheric particulates are produced by cars and trucks; in the U.S.A., motor vehicles are responsible for about 70 percent of total carbon monoxide emissions, 40 percent of nitrogen oxides, and 20 percent of particulates. Lead pollution, a serious health problem in many cities especially in the Third World, is largely attributable to motor vehicle emissions.

Increasing car ownership usually comes at the cost of public transport. Governments often give priority to private motorized travel when it comes to budgets, planning, and urban and rural landscape design. As the emphasis on private transport increases, funding and planning for public transport declines proportionally. This has the effect of further marginalizing people on the economic and social fringes of society — the poor, the elderly, and, especially, women of all classes and ages. Everywhere in the world women are much more dependent than men on public transport, and are less likely to own or even have the use of a car. Car ownership thus both reflects and reinforces social inequities.

The global growth in private car production and ownership is fueled by automobile manufacturers looking to expand their markets. Governments often support the export drives of their domestic car industries and continue to link the spread of car-ownership with development. As rich countries become saturated with automobiles, the Third World beckons. Car culture already has a firm grip on the large cities of Mexico, Brazil, and India, and is making strong inroads almost everywhere else in the developing world.

Sources:
American Automobile Manufacturers' Association. *World Motor Vehicle Data 1993*. Detroit,MI: AAMA,1993; Nadis, Steve and James MacKenzie. *Car Trouble*. Boston: Beacon Press, 1993; Organisation for Economic Cooperation and Development. *OECD Environmental Data Compendium 1993*. Paris: OECD, 1993; Renner, Michael. "Rethinking Transportation" in Lester Brown. ed. *State of the World 1989*. New York: Norton, 1989; Renner, Michael. "Rocky Road Ahead for the Automobile." in Lester Brown. ed. *State of the World 1991*. New York: Norton, 1991; World Resources Institute. *World Resources 1994-95*. New York: Oxford University Press, 1994; World Resources Institute. *World Resources 1992-93*. New York: Oxford University Press, 1992.

10 HOLES IN THE SAFETY NET

A thin layer of ozone, high up in the stratosphere, acts as a shield against harmful solar ultraviolet radiation. Any sustained reduction in ozone, allowing more ultraviolet radiation to reach the earth, will cause considerable harm to human health and to the environment. For example, there will be increases in skin cancers and cataracts, damage to the human immune system, disruption of agriculture and reductions in crop yields, possible large-scale alterations in a number of ecosystems, and disruptions in the marine food chain. Holes in the ozone layer, originally detected in the earth's polar regions, now appear regularly in the lower latitudes over densely populated parts of the world.

Since the mid-1970s, scientists have known that chlorine from synthetic compounds called CFCs (chlorofluorocarbons), and to a lesser extent a number of other chemicals, destroy ozone in the stratosphere. CFCs are artificial compounds, developed in the 1930s, which have been the basis of the development of very powerful and profitable chemical industries. These industries, as well as most governments in CFC-producing countries, originally dismissed the evidence of ozone depletion and, for almost a decade, resisted increasingly urgent calls from the scientific community for curbs in the production of CFC and other ozone-depleting chemicals. The weight of opinion finally shifted in the mid-1980s, and a surprisingly rapid global consensus emerged. The 1987 Montreal Protocol established a schedule for reducing production of ozone-depleting chemicals, and later amendments to the protocol accelerated the timetable. Complete phase-outs of CFCs and halons are now scheduled for the late 1990s, with some scheduling concessions allowed for developing countries.

Most of the ozone-depleting chemicals persist in the upper atmosphere for up to 75 years, however. Therefore even after the use of these chemicals has been eliminated, concentrations in the earth's atmosphere will continue to rise, damaging the ozone layer for decades to follow.

Sources:
Lacoste, Beatrice. "Saving our Ozone Shield." *Our Planet (UNEP)* 4 (4)1992; Lean, Geoffrey and Don Hinrichsen. *Atlas of the Environment*. Oxford: Helicon, 1992; United Nations Environment Programme (UNEP). *Action on Ozone*. UNEP: Nairobi, 1993; United Nations Environment Programme (UNEP).*The Reporting of Data by the Parties to the Montreal Protocol on Substances that deplete the Ozone Layer*. UNEP/Ozone Secretariat: New York,1993.

11 TOURISM

Travel and tourism is the world's largest industry, and one that is expanding all the time. Tourism is increasingly the largest single source of revenue for poor countries, and most governments (rich and poor) actively promote the development of tourist trade. Without tourism, the economies of many of the Caribbean islands, for example, would collapse, as would the economies of many Mediterranean coastal towns.

In some instances, travel and tourism serve to enhance environmental protection. For example, the development of national parks and game reserves in many countries, but most noticeably in Costa Rica and a number of African states, has been spurred on by the promise of attracting tourist revenue. Their maintenance is financed largely by tourism. However, most observers conclude that, on balance, mass tourism is environmentally damaging, especially when it is based on the flow of rich world tourists to the poor world. Tourism has become a quasi-industrial process, in which the landscape, habitat, wildlife and local peoples all become consumable goods. High-volume tourism overwhelms local facilities for water supply, sewage treatment and municipal refuse disposal. Tourist traffic and its related infrastructure threatens fragile environments and often entirely wipes out natural habitats. To serve the tourist trade, many governments have embarked on ambitious programs of road, airport, and hotel construction, often without serious regard for the environmental consequences of these developments. A flourishing wildlife trade often accompanies tourism, as rare and exotic species of birds and animals are hunted in order to sell to tourists — either alive, or as tortoise-shell combs, stuffed-toys made from real fur, brilliantly-colored corals, and the like.

In the late 1980s, another expanding niche in the tourist market was "green" or "eco-tourism." In current usage, eco-tourism means travel to relatively undisturbed areas of natural beauty, an emphasis on environmental protection and the minimizing of traditional tourist needs such as airport and road developments, hotel chains with swimming pools, non-local food and drink, and a souvenir trade. But truly responsible tourism requires radical changes in expectations. Some governments and tour operators are committed to genuine eco-tourism. Others are merely adding a green gloss to their standard package.

Sources:
Boo, Elizabeth. *Ecotourism: The Potentials and Pitfalls.* London: World Wildlife Fund, 1990; Geffen, Alice and Carole Berglie. *EcoTours.* New York: Clarkson Potter, 1993; *The Independent* (London). 5 August 1990; *Sunday Times* (London). 28 June 1992; Tourism Concern, London; United Nations. *Statistical Yearbook 1990-91.* UN:New York, 1993; World Travel and Tourism Council. *Travel and Tourism.* Brussels: WTTC, 1992; World Tourism Organization. *Yearbook of Tourist Statistics.* 45. Geneva, 1993.

12 CURRENT AFFAIRS

In the world economy, fossil fuels provide about 90 percent of all commercial energy used, and their use is growing at the rate of 20 percent per decade. This is bad news for the environment since the burning of fossil fuels is the greatest source of industrial pollution, acid rain, and global warming.

The U.S.A. is by far the largest consumer of commercial energy, but a number of other countries in Western Europe have comparable per capita consumption levels. The rich world uses by far the greatest share of world energy. Industrialized countries use the most energy and almost three times as much commercial energy as developing countries — with less than a quarter of the world's population, they burn about 70 percent of all fossil fuel consumed.

The production, extraction and use of coal, oil, gas, and nuclear power, which together power much of the world, all have destructive environmental consequences. The renewable energy sources most commonly used — hydro and firewood — are more environmentally benign, but still present problems. Firewood is in increasingly short supply, and even though it provides the sole energy source for many Third World households, it may not continue to be a viable energy source into the twenty-first century.

Given this array of destructive sources of energy, conservation policies are vital. After the oil crisis of 1973, the industrial world made systematic efforts to increase energy efficiency. The results were impressive: in the U.S.A., cars now travel 29 percent further on a gallon of gasoline than they did in 1973; in OECD countries, the energy efficiency of industry has improved by about a third since the early 1970s; Denmark was able to reduce its total use of direct fuels by 20 percent between 1976 and 1980. Energy consumption continues to increase, but in industrialized countries the rate of increase has slowed. Denmark, Sweden and Japan are world leaders in energy efficiency.

However, the transfer of energy efficient technology to the Third World has yet to occur, and comparable energy savings there are not even in sight. Developing countries now use 40 percent more energy than first world countries to produce the same value of goods and services. Many energy-intensive industries have relocated from the first world to the Third. Combined with population growth in poorer countries, this means that energy demands in developing countries are expected to triple by 2025.

Many environmentalists argue that conservation is necessary but not sufficient, and that we must radically alter our industries and economies to incorporate large-scale use of solar, geothermal, and wind energy sources, which hold the promise of being both renewable and non-polluting. As yet, these technologies have made little impact on the world's energy budgets, in part because oil companies, nuclear fuel companies and other established energy producers wield considerable influence and can effectively close the energy market to alternatives. Moreover, the commitment to alternative technology and conservation is often weak: in 1986, for example, the OECD member countries spent $622 million on research and development on energy efficiency; in the same year, they spent $4.5 billion on nuclear technologies.

Sources:
British Petroleum. *BP Statistical Review of World Energy*. BP: London, June 1993; Lenssen, Nicholas. "Providing Energy in Developing Countries." in Lester Brown. ed. *State of the World 1993*. New York: Norton, 1993; United Nations. *1990 Energy Statistics Yearbook*. New York: UN,1992; U.S. Office of Technology Assessment. *Fueling Development*. Washington,D.C.: U.S. Office of Technology Assessment,1992; World Resources Institute. *World Resources 1992-93*. New York: Oxford University Press, 1992.

13 NUCLEAR POWER

Electricity generation by nuclear power began in the mid-1950s. Since then, the growth of the industry has been dramatic. There are currently 420 commercial nuclear reactors operating in the world, and more than another 100 planned or on order. In addition to the 31 countries with operating power plants, another two dozen have some form of nuclear facility, such as research reactors. Even though the nuclear industry is widely perceived to pose fundamental health and safety risks, there are actually few signs of its demise. Companies in Western Europe and the U.S.A. (which is the world's largest exporter of nuclear technology,) facing little demand for new power plants at home, are aggressively courting Asian and East European countries in the hope of winning contracts for new plants. Almost half the reactors currently on order are in former Communist bloc states.

Spokespeople for the nuclear industry are quick to point out that nuclear power plants emit none of the greenhouse gases produced by oil and coal power plants. This, however, is a dubious virtue given that the operation of nuclear power plants represents an on-going public health and safety threat, and generates a large volume of highly toxic waste. By 1990, the world had accumulated 84,000 metric tons of irradiated fuel — three times the amount in 1980, and 20 times that of 1970. There is no place to dispose safely of this waste, and fewer places left to store it. Most nuclear states are building up huge stockpiles of nuclear waste that no one wants and no one knows how to get rid of. The UK, the Netherlands, Belgium and Switzerland dumped low-level radioactive waste at sea until 1983 when this practice was halted by an international moratorium under the London Dumping Convention. This agreement is vehemently opposed by the British government, which asserts its right to retain the option of ocean dumping. By the mid-1990s, the UK had dumped approximately 950,000 curies into the world's oceans. The UK's record is beaten only by Russia which continues the Soviet practice of dumping radioactive waste (much from military activities) off its coasts. In total, it is estimated that the former USSR dumped about 2.5 million curies of radioactive waste offshore.

Nuclear states are seeking safe ways to decommission nuclear plants as they become obsolete or unsafe. This will become a significant problem from the mid-1990s, as nuclear power plants built in the 1960s reach the end of their operational life.

The world's worst commercial nuclear reactor accident was at Chernobyl in Ukraine, in 1986. A sizeable portion of Ukraine and most of Belarus was contaminated by this accident, and large areas remain unsafe today. The long-term death toll from the Chernobyl explosion is expected to reach into the thousands. More than two-dozen reactors in the new states of the former USSR are considered to be highly dangerous and unstable, and world nuclear experts say that unless these reactors are shut down or dramatically upgraded, more disasters on the level of Chernobyl are imminent.

Sources:
Bulletin of Atomic Scientists. April 1993 and July/August 1993; Goldsmith,Edward and Nicholas Hildyard. *The Earth Report.* London: Price Sloan, 1988; Lenssen, Nicholas. "Confronting Nuclear Waste." in Lester Brown. ed. *State of the World 1992.* New York: Norton, 1992; *Petroleum Economist.* London 1993; United Nations Environment Programme (UNEP). *Environmental Data Report 1991-92.* Washington, D.C. and London, 1992; U.S. Department of Energy. *Commercial Nuclear Power.* Washington, D.C.: U.S. Department of Energy, 1991; "World List of Nuclear Power Plants." *Nuclear News.* March 1994.

14 OIL

The economies — and lifestyles — of the industrialized world are dependent on oil. Oil is big business, both for private enterprise and state revenue. The transportation of oil to markets and oil-burning for energy are major contributors to fossil fuel pollution. But that is not all. Exploration for oil, which usually takes place in environmentally fragile and sparsely populated areas is a high-risk industrial activity, often causing long-lasting ecological disruption and widespread pollution.

More than six million metric tons of oil are released into the world's oceans each year by oil and other tankers; roughly one ton is spilled for every 1,000 tons extracted. Marine tanker accidents are not the largest source of oil pollution, but they are often the most dangerous, releasing large amounts of oil in a short period of time, often close to shore. The threat posed by single acute oil spills has increased over the past twenty years, as oil companies have switched to larger and larger vessels in an effort to cut costs. Today's "supertankers" average twice the size and carry ten times the amount of oil as tankers that worked the oil routes twenty years ago. On average, there are three maritime oil spills each day, worldwide, but legal and financial responsibility for the ensuing pollution is often difficult to assign. Many oil companies register their ships under "flags of convenience" in such countries as Liberia, the Bahamas, Cyprus or Panama. Such "open registries" allow companies to run ships with lower-cost, non-union crews, to evade certain corporation taxes, and to avoid some national and international regulations. Registries of convenience also obscure the trail of corporate responsibility for accidents and spills.

The chronic release of oil from maritime shipping operations represents an even greater environmental problem than acute spills. On oil supply routes, for example, oil tankers routinely flush out their tanks with sea water on the return trip, in so doing releasing thousands of tons of oil annually. Oily trails around the world mark the major shipping routes.

A primary argument against increased use of renewable energy sources, such as solar power, is that they are much more expensive than oil. However, the true cost of oil is mostly hidden. The real cost of oil dependency must include the expenditures on military forces used to "secure" oil supply routes and oil production regions, federal subsidies and tax allowances for oil companies, the costs of the trade deficits and external debt that most oil-dependent nations now face, and environmental damage and clean-up costs.

Sources:

British Petroleum.*BP Statistical Review of World Energy*. London: BP, June 1993; *The European*. 17-20 December 1992; Gaffney, Cline & Associates, London, UK. personal communication; *The New York Times*. 20 March 1994; Organisation for Economic Cooperation and Development (OECD). *OECD Environmental Data Compendium 1993*. Paris: OECD, 1993; World Resources Institute. *The 1994 Information Please Environmental Almanac*. New York: Houghton Mifflin, 1994.

15 THE DAMMED

The idea of tapping the power of running water is an attractive energy prospect, promising cheap, renewable, and non-polluting energy. However, hydro-electric projects are seldom this simple or benign. Commercial, large-scale production of hydro-electricity typically involves the construction of big dams to trap water in reservoirs, which is then released over a vertical drop in a controlled manner. The reservoirs for large dams are created by flooding vast acreages of land, often inundating valuable forest area, wildlife habitat, wetlands, entire ecological communities, and requiring the relocation of people, towns and cities.

The quality of water in dams often deteriorates, due to a build-up of salts and chemicals, and this threatens crops and drinking supplies. In most dams, the reservoir behind the dam traps silt, and many reservoirs become mires. In warm climates, reservoirs can become breeding grounds for vectors of waterborne disease; throughout Africa, rates of infection from schistosomiasis, and "river blindness" rise dramatically following the construction of most dams.

The construction of a large dam is a huge undertaking. Many of the largest dam projects in the world are funded with assistance from international aid agencies, most notably the World Bank, although there is increasing pressure on the Bank not to continue this sort of funding. In 1950, there were about 5,000 large dams in the world; thirty years later, by the early 1980s, there were 36,000. The frenzy of dam construction appears to have now slowed worldwide, but in the early 1990s several massive dam projects are nevertheless underway, including the Three Gorges dam in China and the James Bay project in Quebec, Canada. The Three Gorges dam will flood hundreds of towns and villages along the Yangtze River; farmland will be lost; the habitat of endangered cranes and the rare, freshwater dolphin – unique to the Yangtse River – will be threatened. The James Bay hydro project will flood an area the size of France and deprive Cree Indians of their hunting grounds.

Information on hydro power and dams is readily available. Pro-dam sources offer mainly detailed records of dam characteristics and construction; anti-dam groups monitor the environmental and social costs of dams.

Sources:

Fearnside,Philip."China's Three Gorges Dam."*World Development* 16 (1988); Gleick, Peter. ed. *Water in Crisis: A Guide to the World's Fresh Water Resources*. New York: Oxford University Press, 1993; International Commission on Large Dams, Paris. personal communication; Natural Resources Defense Council, New York; *Water Power and Dam Construction*. August 1992, January 1993, and May 1993; press reports.

16 THE LONG WALK FOR WOOD

Traditional fuels are local, self-reliant energy sources. Since most statistical information is collected on a national or even international level, information on the supply and use of these fuels is partial, inconsistent, and often based on very small samples. Official reports invariably underestimate rural traditional fuel use. Similarly, information on the amount of time spent collecting firewood — always women's work — must be treated with caution.

Nonetheless, the general situation is clear: many people in many Third World countries rely entirely on traditional fuels — wood, dung, and charcoal — for energy, cooking, and warmth. About 70 to 95 percent of all traditional fuels are used for domestic purposes, and the remainder in cottage industries and small-scale commercial enterprises. Almost everywhere in the world, traditional fuels, especially firewood, are becoming scarce. Much of the world's population faces chronic — and catastrophic — fuelwood shortages.

As shortages become more acute, the effort to collect wood is taking a larger share of the working day. Many women in rural areas report that they are now spending so much time collecting firewood that they have little time for other activities, such as growing and cooking food. With less time to prepare food, simpler diets are adopted — for example, in the Sahel, many women now cook rice instead of millet, and nutrition is suffering.

The firewood crisis has been precipitated by a number of converging factors. Deforestation for commercial logging or for agriculture is a primary cause of localized fuelwood scarcity everywhere in the world. Urban demand is putting pressure on rural resources: for example, firewood for Delhi, India, comes from Madhya Pradesh, 700 kilometres away, and in the late 1980s estimates suggested that six hectares of forest a day had to be cleared just to meet the Delhi demand. Whereas fuelwood for rural uses is often twigs and fallen branches, commercial users will cut down an entire tree.

Sources:

Agarwal, Bina. *Cold Hearths & Barren Slopes: The Fuelwood Crisis in the Third World.* Riverdale, MD: Riverdale Press, 1986; Food and Agriculture Organization (FAO). *Map of the Fuelwood Situation in the Developing Countries.* Rome: FAO, 1981; Food and Agriculture Organization (FAO). *Yearbook of Forest Products, 1984.* Rome: FAO, 1986; Food and Agriculture Organization (FAO). *Yearbook of Forest Products, 1991.* Rome: FAO,1993; Lean, Geoffrey and Don Hinrichsen. *Atlas of the Environment.* Oxford: Helicon, 1992. Myers, Norman. *Gaia: An Atlas of Planet Management.* revised ed. New York: Doubleday, 1993; United Nations. *1990 Energy Statistics Yearbook.* New York: United Nations,1992; U.S. Office of Technology Assessment. *Fueling Development.* Washington, D.C.:Office of Technology Assessment, 1992; World Resources Institute. *World Resources 1994-95.* New York: Oxford University Press, 1994.

17 ACID RAIN

Acid rain is mostly a by-product of industrialization. The "acidification" of precipitation is caused by sulphur and nitrogen emissions from the burning of fossil fuels, notably coal in power stations and oil in motor vehicles. The term "acid rain" includes both the dry deposition of nitrates and sulphates as they settle, and the wet deposition of acidic rain, sleet, snow, or fog. The acidity of a solution is measured in terms of "pH." pH1 is strongly acidic, pH14 strongly alkaline, and pH7 is neutral. Unpolluted precipitation is generally assumed to have a pH value of about 6.

Acid rain spares little. Acid deposition erodes railway tracks, disintegrates ornate historic facades, pits public statues, and corrodes masonry. Natural ecosystems crumble under prolonged exposure to acid rain. Acidification destroys fish life in lakes, kills off forests, and damages crops. To date, acid rain is doing the greatest damage in northern Europe and Canada. Sixty-four percent of the forests in the UK show signs of acid rain damage; in central Switzerland, more than 40 percent of the conifer forests are dead or severely damaged.

Patterns of rainfall and acid deposition show no regard for national borders. Acid deposition has been a contentious issue between the U.S.A. and Canada for years; most acid deposition in the Scandinavian countries, downwind of Europe's major industrial centers, is from other countries; and most of Japan's acid rain comes from China and South Korea.

A concerted European effort to reduce sulphur dioxide emissions has had dramatic results. Many European states ratified a 1985 agreement to reduce emissions by 30 percent by 1993; these reductions were mostly achieved and in many cases surpassed. The European Union has gone even further in mandating that large fossil fuel plants will have to cut emissions of sulphur dioxide by 40 percent by 1998, and by 60 percent by 2003. In the newly industrializing world, acid rain is a growing problem.

Sources:

Elsom, Derek. *Atmospheric Pollution: A Global Problem.* second edition. Oxford and Cambridge, MA: Blackwell, 1993; Myers, Norman. *Gaia: An Atlas of Plant Management.* revised ed. New York: Doubleday,1993; Organisation for Economic Cooperation and Development (OECD). *OECD Environmental Data Compendium 1993.* Paris: OECD, 1993; Park, Chris. *Acid Rain: Rhetoric and Reality.* New York: Methuen, 1987; Peterson, D.J. *Troubled Lands: The Legacy of Soviet Environmental Destruction.* Boulder, CO: Westview Press/RAND Research, 1993; United Nations Economic Commission for Europe. *Strategies and Policies for Air Pollution Abatement, 1993 Review.* September 1993; United Nations Environment Programme (UNEP). *Environmental Data Report, 1991-92.* Washington, D.C. and London: United Nations, 1992.

18 GLOBAL WARMING

Certain gases, including carbon dioxide, methane, nitrous oxides, and chlorofluorocarbons, are accumulating in the upper atmosphere at a faster rate than ever before. Each year, the world pumps about 24 billion tons of carbon and 255 million tons of methane into the atmosphere, mostly from fossil fuel combustion, deforestation, and certain industrial and agricultural practices. Many scientists believe that the accumulation of gases is creating a layer that traps the earth's radiated heat, which will cause global temperatures to rise significantly.

While some other scientists and policy-makers still dispute this conclusion, an international scientific panel convened by the United Nations concluded in 1990 that human activities are altering the atmosphere. If global warming occurs, the predicted consequences include rising sea levels, higher tides, and more violent storms and storm surges. Drinking water supplies may become salinated, agriculture disrupted, vegetation regimes and wildlife habitats adversely affected, and entire islands inundated. Low-lying countries, such as the Netherlands, Bangladesh, the Maldives, and many Pacific island states are especially vulnerable, and may be the first to feel the effects of global warming. Most of the world's major cities and many capital cities are coastal, and even a modest rise in the average sea level would threaten these cities with flooding. Large-scale changes to weather and agricultural patterns would wreak havoc with local livelihoods and national economies.

Strategies to offset global warming focus on reducing the use of fossil fuels, eliminating CFCs, and trying to halt further global deforestation. Such an agenda has sweeping implications. It requires changes in industrial lifestyles and economies, and its impact on the economic expansion of poor countries is difficult to assess. The enormity of the implications of global warming is creating sharp controversy in scientific circles and this is impeding international action.

Sources:

Marshall, Bruce. ed. *The Real World.* Boston: Houghton Mifflin, 1991; Myers, Norman. *Gaia: An Atlas of Planet Management.* revised ed. New York: Doubleday, 1993; U.S. Office of Technology Assessment. *Fueling Development.* Washington, D.C.: Office of Technology Assessment, 1992; World Resources Institute. *World Resources 1992-93.* New York: Oxford University Press, 1992; World Wide Fund for Nature. "Can Nature Survive Global Warming?" International Discussion Paper. February 1992. Gland, Switzerland,1992.

19 INDUSTRIAL WASTELANDS

Throughout Eastern Europe and the former USSR, the "military-industrial complex" operated for decades to maximize industrial output with scant regard for the environment. Consequently, much of the area now suffers virtually irreparable ecological damage, and the landscape is scarred with industrial wastelands. Outrage over these environmental conditions was one of the major catalysts of the political agitation in the late 1980s that eventually led to the disintegration of the USSR. In the mid-1990s, however, in the face of traumatic social and economic realignments, the environment seems to have slipped down the policy-makers' agenda.

The largest single output of all manufacturing industry is pollution. The former USSR serves as the most extreme example of the impact of untrammelled industrialization but everywhere in the world industrial activity generates millions of tons of waste and much of it is extremely toxic. No state has effective constraints or regulations to control the excesses of industry, and decision-makers in the industrial world appear to be largely unwilling to police themselves.

Industrial pollution is ubiquitous but detailed information on its extent, nature, and origin is typically spotty and much of it remains unidentified. The "blighted zones" identified on the world map represent the most extreme cases of industrial pollution; thousands more zones of localized blight scar every industrialized country and would need to be mapped on a regional scale.

The extent of industrial pollution around the world is alarming. Some 350 million metric tons of hazardous industrial wastes are generated worldwide each year, about 90 percent of which comes from industrial countries. There are no good ways to get rid of waste, especially hazardous waste. In the U.S.A., the Environmental Protection Agency has identified a top-priority national list of over 5,000 hazardous sites ("Superfund sites") left behind by industry, which, if they can be cleaned up at all, will cost billions of dollars.

The world map identifies major accidents between 1985 and 1993 that have occurred during the manufacture and transport of hazardous industrial products — it does not include accidents that occur in the end use and application of those materials. There are several biases: as ever, the data mostly refer to accidents in the developed world, and by definition, these lists focus on acute events, not chronic releases. Industrial accidents involving the release of hazardous substances are a daily occurrence, but record-keeping is inadequate. Only large and spectacular accidents, such as the explosion of gas tanks in Mexico City in 1984, attract international attention, and most smaller-scale accidents do not even attract notice from the national press. Several quasi-official groups attempt to monitor accidents in the U.S.A. — the Acute Hazardous Events Data Base and the National Response Center of the Department of Transportation among them — but few other countries have systems for tracking industrial accidents. What we do know for certain about industrial accidents is that they have become adjuncts of an industrial culture.

Sources:
Organisation for Economic Cooperation and Development (OECD). *OECD Environmental Data Compendium 1993*. Paris: OECD, 1993; Peterson, D.J. *Troubled Lands: The Legacy of Soviet Environmental Destruction*. Boulder, CO: Westview Press, 1993; Russian Academy of Sciences. Institute of Geography, Moscow.

20 THE FARMING FIX

The use of fertilizer is monitored closely by the UN's Food and Agriculture Organization. World fertilizer consumption in 1991 was approximately 135 million tons. The use of agro-chemicals has increased tenfold since World War II, and most crops in the world are now grown with the assistance of artificial fertilizers and biocides.

Since the 1950s, the spread of fertilizers has escalated with the spread of Western-style agriculture into poor countries, coupled with a move towards commodity-export agriculture in the same countries. (These trends have been encouraged and in some cases mandated by international aid and development agencies.) And in China, where economic reforms begun in the late 1970s converted the agriculture sector to a market economy, there has been a dramatic increase in fertilizer use. Worldwide, fertilizer use peaked in the late 1980s and now appears to be declining. Few anticipated this global decline, most of which can probably be attributed to reduced fertilizer use in the new states of the former USSR following the removal of heavy subsidies.

Commercial fertilizers, many of which are petroleum-based, are expensive. Once a farming system is dependent on commercial inputs, it is expensive to maintain, but difficult to stop. Use of commercial fertilizers does usually increase crop productivity in the short run; it is becoming clear, however, that gains in productivity are not sustained. The use of artificial inputs is self-perpetuating: to compensate for disruptions in soil ecology caused by heavy fertilizer use, farmers typically turn to the use of herbicides, insecticides, and pesticides; the use of these chemicals strips soils of nutrients, which in turn calls for heavier applications of fertilizers. Thus a cycle of addiction is set in motion, and one that produces diminishing returns.

Sources:
Food and Agriculture Organization (FAO). *Fertilizer Yearbook 1992.* Rome: FAO, 1993; World Resources Institute. *World Resources 1994-95.* New York: Oxford University Press, 1994; Worldwatch Institute/Lester Brown. ed. *Vital Signs 1993.* New York: Norton, 1993.

21 BUGS AND DRUGS

Pesticides are used in agriculture for pest, weed, and plant disease control. They are also important in the control of infectious diseases, such as malaria. In the Third World, damage by pests may cause crop losses of up to 75 percent. However, the cost of pesticides is high and their efficiency is limited.

In 1962, an American scientist, Rachel Carson, alerted the world to the dangers of pesticides: "What we have to face is not an occasional dose of poison which has accidentally got into some article of food, but a consistent and continuous poisoning of the whole human environment." Of the 23 pesticides that Carson identified as particularly hazardous, two-thirds are still in use around the world today. For example, DDT nearly wiped out dozens of domestic bird species on the eastern seaboard of the U.S.A. before its use was banned in the early 1970s; in Thailand, DDT is now threatening drinking supplies throughout the country; over large regions of Central America, where pesticide use levels are among the highest in the world, wildlife has been decimated and the natural ecology is struggling.

Pesticides can create a variety of environmental problems. They cause widespread surface and groundwater pollution from chemical runoff from croplands. Some harmful chemical residues pass into the food chain. Insecticides and herbicides are wide-spectrum biocides that kill more "benign" animals and birds than "pests." Farmworkers are frequently posioned by pesticides. In the U.S.A., the Environmental Protection Agency estimates that at least 66 of the 300 or so pesticide ingredients commonly used by farmers are "probable carcinogens," and dozens more are known to cause birth defects, nervous system disorders, and other chronic illnesses; accidents in the manufacture and storage of agro-chemicals have killed thousands of people worldwide and caused grave environmental damage. Many of the major industrial accidents in the past 20 years have involved agro-chemical production facilities: among the most prominent of these have been the accidents at Seveso, Italy in 1976, Bhopal, India in 1984, and the Sandoz chemical spill into the Rhine River in 1986.

The benefits of using pesticides are in many cases short-lived. While insecticide use in the U.S.A., for example, has increased more than ten times since 1945, pest damage to crops has more than doubled. Worldwide, the percentage of crop loss from pest damage has not measurably declined in the last 50 years, despite the introduction and massive use of pesticides during this period.

Although the dangers of agricultural chemicals are well known, the chemical lobby is powerful enough to evade or defeat most efforts to regulate their products. When domestic regulation threatens chemical production, a company will sometimes relocate to another country or simply turn to other markets: current estimates suggest that 75 percent of the pesticides used in the Third World would not be allowed in the U.S.A. Many of the chemicals used by farmers in poorer countries are banned in first world markets, but produced by American and West European firms for use overseas.

Sources
Agrow World Crop Production News (London) 165 (August) 1992; Carson, Rachel. *Silent Spring.* London: Penguin Books, 1990; Food and Agriculture Organization (FAO). *Trade Yearbook 1992.* Rome: FAO, 1993; Gleick, Peter. ed. *Water in Crisis: A Guide to the World's Fresh Water Resources.* New York: Oxford University Press, 1993; Organisation for Economic Cooperation and Developmen (OECD). *OECD Environmental Data Compendium 1993.* Paris: OECD, 1993; The Pesticides Trust. *The Pesticide Hazard.* London: Zed Press, 1993.

22 TOXIC TRADE

Industrialized countries produce over 300 million metric tons of hazardous waste each year. These wastes pose a threat to human and animal health, and countless towns and local habitats around the world have been poisoned by improper disposal of toxins. The dilemma of toxic waste is that there is no completely safe way to dispose of it: if it is dumped in landfills or storage pits, poisons inevitably leak out into drinking water and residential areas; if it is burned, it leaves a toxic residue; if it is dumped at sea (a process now banned by most countries), it threatens marine mammal and fish life.

In lieu of solving the waste problem — which can only really be solved by reducing the production of toxins at source — many governments and private firms have chosen to simply ship it away, out of sight, out of mind. Over the past decade, poor countries have been targetted to be the main recipients of the rich world's industrial waste. Much of the trade has been illicit or illegal, and its extent is difficult to determine. The international waste disposal business is a shady one: there have been many cases of toxic shipments being illegally dumped on the shores of poor countries; in others, governments of Third World countries are deliberately misled about the nature of the proposed waste shipments. In the late 1980s, poor countries organized a fierce resistance to this "trade." Importing hazardous waste is now banned by more than 100 states, including virtually the whole of Africa.

It has been more difficult to get rich industrial states to agree to control their waste exports, but in 1994 most (excepting the U.S.A.) agreed to ban the export of hazardous or poisonous wastes to poor states. Trade among industrialized countries is not affected by this agreement. Many industrial countries exchange waste, although the flow of trade still typically reflects power imbalances between exporters and importers. Canada receives a large share of toxic waste from the U.S.A.; Hungary and the UK are major repositories for European waste; China accepts waste from the U.S.A. and from Europe. This trade may be more consensual than Third World dumping, but it is no less dangerous.

Eastern Europe and the new states of the former USSR have become new dumping grounds for hazardous waste. The flow into these countries is largely unregulated, and all indications suggest that this trade is increasingly controlled by organized crime within the former USSR. Although the 1994 export ban by rich countries is intended to include shipments to Eastern Europe, it is unlikely that this trade will be halted.

Sources:
Buzzworm. ed. *1993 Earth Journal.* Boulder, CO: Buzzworm Books, 1992; Greenpeace U.S.A. *Toxic Trade Campaign.* various reports, including quarterly reports in *Toxic Trade Update.* Lean, Geoffrey and Don Hinrichsen. *Atlas of the Environment.* Oxford: Helicon, 1992; Organisation for Economic Cooperation and Development (OECD). *OECD Environmental Data Compendium 1993.* Paris: OECD, 1993; United Nations Environment Programme (UNEP). *Environmental Data Report 1991-92.* Washington, D.C. and London, 1992.

23 ATOMIC ATOLLS

Many states see the Pacific as a convenient "empty place" on the planet for weapons testing, waste dumping, and other activities that would not be tolerated or considered safe if carried out nearer their own centers of population. As the map shows, this has had deadly consequences for many small island states in the Pacific, and for the thousands of people who live there.

The Pacific has borne the heavy brunt of the nuclear weapons race during the decades of the Cold War; most of the nuclear weapons systems stationed in Europe and the U.S.A. have been tested on the lands of indigenous peoples in the Pacific, without their informed consent and often without warning. Britain tested its earliest nuclear weapons in Australia in the 1950s and, as this practice became controversial, shifted its H-bomb tests to Christmas and Malden islands in the Pacific in the late 1950s. France began testing nuclear weapons in its French Polynesia territories in the early 1960s, after it lost the war in Algeria and, with that defeat, lost access to its earlier testing grounds in the Algerian Sahara. The United States' military was responsible for more than 200 nuclear explosions in the Pacific from the 1940s to the 1960s. Of these three nuclear states, only France continues to test nuclear weapons in the Pacific, but the U.S.A. continues to use the Pacific for a range of military purposes, including missile testing and chemical weapons incineration.

Many of the islands in the Pacific consist of fragile coral atolls. These are rings of coral, barely above sea level, surrounding a central lagoon. One of the consequences of the extensive nuclear testing here is that entire atolls have been "vaporized;" other atolls are so radioactive that they will remain uninhabitable for thousands of years. The populations of many Pacific territories have been displaced and have become environmental refugees. Rates of certain cancers associated with radiation exposure, such as thyroid cancer, have been escalating among the populations of Pacific islanders who were exposed to nuclear tests.

The Pacific nuclear-free movement, largely a women's movement, is now one of the most active grassroots anti-nuclear campaigns in the world.

Sources:
Dibblin, Jane. *The Day of Two Suns*. London: Virago, 1988; Hayes, Peter. et al. *American Lake: Nuclear Peril in the Pacific*. London: Penguin, 1986; Kidron, Michael and Dan Smith. *The New State of War and Peace*. New York: Simon and Schuster; London: HarperCollins, 1991; Seager, Joni. *Earth Follies: Coming to Feminist Terms With the Global Environmental Crisis*. New York: Routledge, 1993; Women Working for a Nuclear Free and Independent Pacific. *Pacific Women Speak: Why Haven't You Known?* Oxford: Green Line, 1987.

24 WAR AND PEACE

The world's militaries are egregious environmental offenders. And the bigger and more powerful the militaries, the worse their environmental record. In conducting wars and in their constant preparations for wars, militaries consume disproportionate shares of resources, produce vast quantities of pollutants, and leave toxic footprints wherever they go.

Wars are acutely destructive to the environment. Often, as in Vietnam in the 1960s and 1970s, Central America in the 1980s, and the Persian Gulf in the 1990s, the natural environment is itself a military target. Even when the environment is not deliberately targeted, it inevitably suffers "collateral damage" from war. Agricultural areas become unworkable as villages are destroyed, farming families are killed or forced to flee, crops and livestock are seized or destroyed. Large tracts of land are strewn with mines or with unexploded bombs and shells.

In terms of the natural environment, the price of militarized peace is nearly as high as the cost of war. Virtually every military installation in the world that is used for the development, production, storage, transport or deployment of weapons and related military material poses an environmental hazard. Nuclear facilities are especially hazardous. Recent revelations in the international media underscore the enormity of the environmental damage caused by military nuclear facilities, especially in the two former superpowers of the world. In the U.S.A., leaks of radioactive materials from the Rocky Flats facility threaten the drinking water supply of Denver, Colorado; the Fernald materials production plant in Ohio has released hundreds of tons of uranium dust into the surrounding air and water; and, the agricultural land around Hanford, Washington, shows high levels of radiation. Throughout the former USSR, wide regions and dozens of communities have been polluted by military radioactive dumping and testing; the environmental threats posed by repeated USSR (and now, Russian) dumping of nuclear waste at sea have yet to be assessed. As the layers of secrecy from the Cold War are peeled away, it becomes clear that in the name of protecting people, the militaries of the world are poisoning them.

It is difficult to present a comprehensive assessment of the environmental impacts of militarism because much of the relevant information is kept secret by military and government bureaucracies. Thus the information presented on these two maps represents only the tip of the iceberg.

Sources:

Peterson, D.J. *Troubled Lands: The Legacy of Soviet Environmental Destruction.* Boulder, CO: Westview Press, 1993; Renner, Michael. "Preparing for Peace." in Lester Brown. ed. *State of the World 1993.* New York: Norton, 1993; Renner, Michael. "Cleaning up after the Arms Race." in Lester Brown. ed. *State of the World 1994.* New York: Norton, 1994; Seager, Joni. *Earth Follies: Coming to Feminist Terms With the Global Environmental Crisis.* New York: Routledge, 1993; Shulman, Seth. *The Threat at Home: Confronting the Toxic Legacy of the U.S. Military.* Boston: Beacon Press, 1992; press reports.

25 UNDER THE SEA

The world's oceans are suffering myriad environmental assaults: fisheries have been driven to the point of collapse, pollution along the world's coasts and beaches has become the norm, oceans are still considered to be convenient dumping grounds by many states, marine mammals are dying in unprecedented numbers, and coral reefs — the marine equivalent of tropical forests — are threatened in almost all parts of the globe.

However, there are some promising signs that the tide is slowly turning. The construction of sewage facilities in many countries is reducing a significant source of ocean pollution; one recent international agreement bans the use of driftnet fishing, while another provides whale sanctuaries in the Antarctic and Indian Oceans; and agreements to end ocean dumping of industrial and nuclear wastes have been signed by increasing numbers of governments.

Fish is a major source of food — fisheries supply almost 20 percent of the world's protein — and fishing provides a livelihood for millions of people. Since 1950, global yields of fish (both marine and fresh-water) have risen over fourfold, from 20 million tonnes to more than 85 million metric tons. However, world fish stocks are now threatened by a number of forces, including over-exploitation, pollution, and wetlands destruction, and yields in many fisheries are declining precipitously. According to one FAO survey, many of the world's fishing grounds are now over-fished to the point of collapse. The cod fishery of the Canadian Grand Banks, for example, once one of the richest in the world, is now commercially dead and may even be biologically dead.

Nearly one-third of all fish species live on coral reefs, and reefs are home to perhaps one-quarter of all marine species. Coral reefs are fragile and the slightest damage can kill large areas of the reef, and the marine life it supports. Corals are under threat in most parts of the world from any number of assaults: pollution; smothering from silt carried to coastal waters from inland rivers, often aggravated by upstream deforestation; the luxury trade in ornamental corals; damage from boats and divers; the mining of reefs to make cement or road-building material. Many marine scientists now say that only reefs in remote regions are healthy and, without immediate action, up to 70 percent of the world's coral reefs may be lost in the next half-century.

Sources:
Food and Agriculture Organization (FAO). *Review of the State of the World's Fisheries.* Circular 710. Rome: FAO, 1992;   Myers, Norman. *Gaia: An Atlas of Planet Management.* revised ed. New York: Doubleday, 1993; United Nations Environment Programme (UNEP). *The State of the Marine Environment.* New York: United Nations, 1990; Weber, Peter. "Safeguarding Oceans." in Lester Brown. ed. *State of the World 1994.* New York: Norton, 1994; Weber, Peter. "Reviving Coral Reefs." in Lester Brown. ed. *State of the World 1993.* New York: Norton, 1993; World Resources Institute. *World Resources 1992-93.* New York: Oxford University Press, 1992; press reports.

26 WETLANDS

Wetlands are found from the tropics to the tundra, and in total cover about six percent of the earth's surface. Comparable data on wetlands extent and loss is difficult to assemble, in part because there is considerable latitude in defining what constitutes a wetland; ecologists recognize more than a dozen wetland types, including marshes, fens, bogs, mires, mangroves, prairie potholes, swamps, and muskeg.

Wetlands are crucial to maintaining the health of the planet. Coastal wetlands (mangroves in the tropics and subtropics, and salt marshes in the temperate zones) are especially important: they serve as huge reservoirs of diverse species, and provide rich wildlife habitats for birds, animals, and fish. They are also the spawning grounds for most of the world's commercial fisheries. Coastal wetlands act as natural buffers that temper the effects of extreme flooding and drought; they filter pollutants out of maritime systems, recharge groundwater drinking supplies, and stabilize coastal erosion.

Logging and agricultural drainage are perhaps the greatest global threats to wetlands, but pollution and urban development rank close behind. Urban development has claimed almost half the wetlands in the U.S.A. as a whole. South-East Asia has the largest mangrove ecosystem in the world, but it is rapidly being cleared for commercial logging and shrimp farming.

The consequences of wetlands loss cannot be fully controlled by individual states, nor do they end at state boundaries. For example, the migrating birds of Western Europe depend on wetlands in north Africa for refuge during their journey; and in the U.S.A., the drainage of wetlands in Louisiana threatens the fisheries of the entire Gulf of Mexico.

Wetlands need to be restored, not merely preserved, and several countries, including Israel and the U.S.A., launched ambitious reclamation programs in the early 1990s. Since 1971, some measure of international wetlands protection has been offered through the Convention on Wetlands of International Significance (also known as the "Ramsar Convention.)" But many states have neither designated nor reported their wetlands and less than two percent of the world's total is protected under this convention.

Sources:
Dugan, Patric. ed. *Wetlands in Danger.* New York: Oxford University Press, 1993; Gleick, Peter. ed. *Water in Crisis: A Guide to the World's Fresh Water Resources.* New York: Oxford University Press,1993; Williams, Michael. ed. *Wetlands: A Threatened Landscape.* London: Basil Blackwell, 1990; World Resources Institute. *World Resources 1994-95.* New York: Oxford University Press, 1994; World Resources Institute. *The 1994 Information Please Environmental Almanac.* New York: Houghton Mifflin, 1994.

27 FORESTS AND RAINFORESTS

Tropical rainforests originally covered an estimated 16 million square kilometres (or six million square miles) of the world; today, probably less than half remains. Although tropical forests comprise only a third of the world's total forest, they contain four-fifths of the world's vegetation: a single hectare of primary forest may support plant material weighing anywhere from 300 to 500 tons. Tropical forests provide habitat for an estimated 50 percent of the world's animal and bird species. As tropical forests are destroyed, so other plant and animal life will disappear too.

There are many causes of tropical forest loss: commercial logging; migration of poor farming families into forests, often as part of government-promoted relocation schemes; conversion of forest land into commercial cash cropland, usually to grow beef or soya, and often to raise capital to pay off foreign debts; and, firewood collection and charcoal production. Commercial logging is responsible for some of the greatest losses. The tropical forests of the world are rich in highly-prized, "luxury" woods such as teak, mahogany, and balsa, among dozens of others. Extracting this timber is a profitable business. Most commercial logging operations in the tropics are monopolized by a handful of multinational timber conglomerates based in France, Germany, the UK, and Japan; in many countries, the timber trade is controlled by militaries or armed insurgents who are using the sale of rare woods to finance wars. Logging operations in most tropical forests are generally characterized by poor planning, poor management, and sweeping environmental degradation. At the current rate of deforestation most experts predict that virtually all remaining tropical forests will disappear within 40 years. By 2010, there will be very little forest left in Asia, and East and West Africa, almost none left in Central America, and in South America the only remaining large areas of forest will be in western Brazil and the Guyana highlands. The tropical forests of the Côte d'Ivoire, Nigeria, India, and Thailand are already essentially depleted.

Tropical rainforest destruction has highlighted an important issue of social justice: the land rights of indigenous peoples. Large numbers of tribal people each year are losing their lands in the name of development and progress. In the heart of Borneo, Brazil, the Philippines, and Malaysia, tribal peoples have been fighting to protect their rainforest homelands.

While the world's attention has focused on deforestation in the tropics, the loss and degradation of temperate forests is also of considerable environmental importance. Old-growth forests in Europe, North America and Australia have been virtually eliminated, and pitched battles are now raging over protection of the remaining forests. The forests of Siberia are the largest in the world and more than half have never been logged. But for multinational timber companies (especially those in South Korea and the U.S.A.), Siberia is the newest logging frontier. And because the Russian government has been slow to regulate logging, clearcutting in Siberia is accelerating rapidly.

The recent recognition that the world's large forested areas, both temperate and tropical, influence the global climate, and may counter the effects of global warming, has raised the stakes around forest protection. To halt large-scale deforestation will require sustained international cooperation, as well as effective regulation of multinational agricultural and logging industries. As of the mid-1990s, there is still no coordinating body for international forest protection and management.

Reliable estimates of rates of deforestation are difficult to determine. For one thing, deforestation itself means different things to different people. To the logging industries, deforestation is the loss of commercial timber stock. To environmentalists, deforestation implies the destruction of a forest ecosystem, which can occur even if stands of trees remain.

Sources:

Buzzworm. ed. *1993 Earth Journal.* Boulder, CO: Buzzworm Books, 1992; Food and Agriculture Organization (FAO) *Forest Products Yearbook 1991.* Rome: FAO, 1993; Myers, Norman and Richard A. Houghton. *Deforestation Rates in Tropical Forests and their Climatic Implications.* London: Friends of the Earth, 1989; Pulp and Paper International. *1992 North American Fact Book.* San Francisco, CA: Pulp and Paper, 1991; United Nations Environment Programme (UNEP). *Environmental Data Report, 1991-92.* Washington, D.C. and London: United Nations, 1992; World Resources Institute. *World Resources 1994-95.* New York: Oxford University Press, 1994.

28 LOSING GROUND

Soil degradation is a broad term which refers to a loss of soil productivity through processes such as compaction, desertification, erosion, or salination . This is a pressing global concern. Soil is an essentially non-renewable resource: it can take up to 12,000 years to build enough soil to form productive farmland. Soil degradation is threatening agricultural viability on all six continents. The FAO reports that the world is losing up to 17.5 million acres (an area nearly as large as Ireland) of fertile land every year due to soil degradation. Millions more acres are only marginally productive or irreparably desertified.

"Desertification" was a prominent environmental issue in the 1970s and early 1980s. Described as a problem of over-exploitation of marginal lands in arid climates (especially in the Sahel area of Africa), the term conjured up images of "deserts on the march". The concept itself has come under much critical review, but as part of a larger soil degradation process, desertification remains a serious problem in many parts of the world.

Erosion — the removal of soil by wind or water — is a natural and on-going process, but one that is dramatically aggravated and advanced by human activity, particularly the removal of vegetation. When forests are cut down or land is cleared for agriculture or animal grazing, there is nothing left to stabilize the soil, and rapid soil loss follows. The deadly land-slides and floods that have plagued many Himalayan states, and Bangladesh in particular, are largely attributed to the linked problems of deforestation and erosion. In Australia, six metric tons of topsoil are eroded for every ton of produce grown; in the U.S.A., a third of all cropland is affected by erosion; over much of Asia, 40 percent of the land is at high risk of erosion and desertification.

Traditional peasant farming systems are often blamed for erosion problems. A more serious factor is the spread of mechanized farming and the introduction of vast livestock ranges that has led to overgrazing and unsustainable intensive agriculture. Overgrazing is the single most prominent cause of soil damage, responsible for 35 percent of soil degradation worldwide.

Sources:
Crump, Andy. *Dictionary of Environment and Development.* London: Earthscan,1991; Food and Agriculture Organization (FAO). *Protect and Produce.* revised ed. Rome: FAO, 1993; Gleick, Peter. ed.*Water in Crisis: A Guide to the World's Fresh Water Resources.* New York: Oxford University Press, 1993; World Resources Institute. *World Resources 1992-93.* New York: Oxford University Press, 1992.

29 SHRINKING SPECIES

We are in the midst of the largest episode of animal and plant extinction in 65 million years, the only equivalent being the period of dinosaur extinctions. While extinctions are part of the natural order, the destruction of natural habitat (particularly through deforestation and expansion of settlements,) hunting, and the luxury trade in animals and plants are responsible for their spiraling scale. By the year 2000, between 40,000 and 50,000 animal species will be lost annually.

Information about the world's animal communities and their levels of survival is very uneven. Generally, more is known about the situation in richer, industrialized countries, and less is known about countries such as Zaire and Brazil — which are species-rich, but poor in scientific monitoring resources. The data is uneven in other important respects. More money is available to fund studies of large mammals and primates (perhaps because of their perceived kinship and "usefulness" to humans.) Little attention is given to less attractive animals and birds, and even less to insects or fish. Thus, there is not even a "best estimate" available for the number of insects being lost to extinction, and only vague estimates of losses in bird, reptile and fish populations.

Birds are especially vulnerable to extinction because they are migratory and range over a wide territory. Coordinated international action is needed for the protection of birds but this is difficult to achieve. For example, the annual hunting massacre of millions of songbirds along their migration paths in the Mediterranean has gained considerable notoriety and drawn protests from the European Union, but has not yet been halted. A third of Europe's birds are threatened with extinction, of which hunting is a major cause, followed by habitat destruction. Hunters, who kill an estimated 900 million migrating birds each year, justify the slaughter as a male ritual with links to cultural traditions that go back thousands of years.

All life on the planet depends, directly or indirectly, on plants. And yet plant species are being destroyed at an alarming rate. If present rates of habitat destruction continue, then some 40,000 to 60,000 plants will face extinction within the next 50 years. Beyond this broad understanding, however, the specifics of plant extinctions are more difficult to assess — which is why there has been no attempt to map them here. While there is substantial knowledge of threatened plants in some countries, there is almost no plant inventory or assessment for key countries such as Brazil, much of Central America, and most of Africa. The Threatened Plants Unit of the International Union for Conservation of Nature (IUCN) in the UK collects the only available international database on plants, and publishes a floristic inventory in their "Red Data Books." Red Books have so far been compiled for more than 70 countries and islands.

The destruction of plants will undermine medical advances. Eighty percent of the world's population depends on natural plant sources for medicinal remedies, and even in high-technology Western medicine, a very high proportion of life-saving drugs are initially derived from plant sources and then synthesized for large-scale production. Destruction of the plant genetic resource pool threatens agriculture; most of the world's food comes from 20 plant species which are already suffering a rapid decline in genetic diversity.

Environmentalist Norman Myers offers this summing-up: "Unwittingly for the most part, but right around the world, we are eliminating the panoply of life. We elbow species off the planet, we deny room to entire communities of nature, we domesticate the Earth. With growing energy and ingenuity, we surpass ourselves time and again to exert dominion over fowl and fish....Eventually we may achieve our aim, by eliminating every other competitor for living space on the crowded Earth. When the last creature is accounted for, we shall have made ourselves masters of all creation. We shall look around and we shall see nothing but each other. Alone at last."

Sources:
Myers, Norman. ed. *Gaia: An Atlas of Planet Management.* New York: Doubleday, 1984; World Resources Institute. *World Resources 1994-95.* New York: Oxford University Press, 1994.

30 IN FOR THE KILL

Today comparatively few human populations meet their basic food and clothing needs by hunting; and those that do so leave relatively few marks on the ecosystem. This map focuses on recreational hunting, whether for "sport" alone or to supply the luxury trade in wildlife.

Recreational hunters often defend their sport by saying that it is a celebration of nature, but the record speaks otherwise. Around the world, recreational hunting has pushed hundreds of species to the brink of extinction, and in recent times, dozens more have been hunted out of existence. Some of the endangered species shown on the map are almost extinct already: for example, there remain only about 100 Sumatran rhino and an estimated 500 Siberian tigers in the world.

Hunting is big business. Apart from the considerable sums of money sometimes paid for the trophy hunting of rare mammals (or for trophy parts of these animals, such as a gorilla's paw or rhino's horn,) the ordinary business of hunting generates considerable revenues: hunters in the

U.S.A., for example, spend an estimated $16 billion annually on fees and equipment. In poor countries, such as Zimbabwe and Zambia, hunting is one of the major sources of revenue earned from rich foreigners. Everywhere, hunting is primarily a men's activity, and is often construed as a rite of passage into manhood.

The figures on U.S. big-game killings abroad are derived from import records maintained by the U.S. Fish and Wildlife Service. The tally shown on the map represents the official record for seven big-game animals hunted abroad and legally imported into the U.S.A. as trophies during a 19-month period. Thus, this represents just a small portion of the whole. Germans, Australians, Taiwanese and Saudi Arabians, among others, swell the ranks of big-game hunters, but few countries keep equivalent records.

Sources:

Burton, J.A. and B. Pearson. *Rare Mammals of the World*. New York and London: Collins, 1987; Cetacean Society International, Georgetown, CT. personal communication; Federation of Field Sports Associations of the European Union, Brussels. personal communication; International Union for Conservation of Nature (IUCN). *The 1990 IUCN Red List of Threatened Animals*. London and Cambridge, MA: IUCN, 1990; U.S.A. Fish and Wildlife Service. "Wildlife Import Declarations." Annual compilation, n.d.; World Wildlife Fund. "Top 10 Most Wanted." (March newsletter). Washington, D.C.: WWF, 1993.

31 THE WILD TRADE

The Convention on International Trade in Endangered Species (CITES) monitors the wildlife trade, and imposes restraints on the trade in certain animals designated for protection. Currently, trade is officially banned for about 700 species (identified as "Appendix I" species,) and regulated for at least 27,000 more ("Appendix II" species.) CITES figures are the best available, but are known to be underestimates. Although CITES does make estimates of the extent of illegal trade, it is almost impossible to verify these figures. The representation of CITES statistics on this map includes the secondary trade in processed animal products and the re-export traffic — thus, some countries are identified as both major exporters and importers of the same animals.

The legal traffic in wildlife is worth about $5 billion annually, and illegal trade is estimated to be about a third as large again. The trade in wildlife is almost entirely a luxury trade: the demand comes from rich countries, and the supply from poor countries. To the brokers in wealthier countries, animals are merely exotic objects to be traded as expensive baubles, such as aphrodisiacs or ivory-handled daggers. While to many traders in poor countries, wildlife is all there is left to sell.

The traffic in animals is mainly a male enterprise. Usually the hunters or poachers are men, as are the safari organizers, the brokers and the buyers.

Sources:

Lean, Geoffrey and Don Hinrichsen. *Atlas of the Environment*. Oxford: Helicon, 1992; TRAFFIC USA. *Annual Imports of Wildlife*. Washington, D.C.: TRAFFIC, 1993; World Resources Institute. *World Resources 1994-95*. New York: Oxford University Press, 1994; World Conservation Monitoring Centre, London; press reports.

32 HEALTH WARNINGS

Many of the topics covered in this atlas have implications for human health. In the course of an ordinary day, we encounter a barrage of chemicals, most of them invisible and many of them unknown — in our workplaces, on the streets, in our food, and in our homes. Along with the rest of the natural world, people suffer from the effects of environmental damage.

However, specific and definitive links between human health and environmental damage are often difficult to establish. As yet, few environmental problems are unequivocally identified with specific health consequences, although the depletion of the ozone layer is known to cause rising rates of skin cancer; and escalating car traffic is raising lead levels in the blood of most inhabitants of most large cities. But there are signs that exposure to certain chemicals and low-level radiation can be either a principal or partial cause of certain types of cancer, even if specific links have yet to be uncovered. The primary cause of lung cancer, the most common cancer in the developed world, is smoking, but it is also known that there can be other contributory factors, including occupational hazards and chemical exposures. As the lifestyles and environmental problems of the industrial world spread around the globe, so too will "modern" cancers.

General health statistics are readily available for most rich states, but for most others they are much more difficult to obtain. But in almost all cases, internationally available health statistics are rarely presented or discussed in terms of contributing causes. Environmental causality, which must be superimposed on basic health data, may be best illustrated on the level of very specific and closely-analysed case studies, rather than on a national or international level.

Sources:

Godlee, Fiona and Alison Walker. *Health and the Environment.* London: BMJ, 1992; Greenpeace U.S.A. *Chlorine, Human Health and the Environment: The Breast-Cancer Warning.* New York: Greenpeace, 1993; United Nations Environment Programme/GEMS Environmental Library. *Urban Air Pollution.* 4. 1991; World Resources Institute. *The 1994 Information Please Environmental Almanac.* New York: Houghton Mifflin, 1994; press reports.

33 PROTECTED PLACES

In virtually every country in the world, some natural areas and sites are protected from human incursions such as hunting, logging, and urban development. In itself, the designation of protected lands can be taken as an indicator of environmental commitment, but in reality "protection" is often neither rigorously enforced nor maintained. Poor countries, in particular, tend to lack the financial and scientific resources necessary for maintaining natural sites, and in many countries the regulatory mechanisms for protection are weak.

The percentage of land area designated for protection shown on the main map was calculated by adding together the land area in each country which has been put aside for scientific reserves, national parks, natural monuments or landmarks, and managed natural reserves (that is, categories I-IV of the IUCN's land use classification system.)

The World Heritage List, established under the terms of UNESCO's 1972 convention, is a register of the world's outstanding natural and cultural heritage. By the early 1990s over 130 governments were parties to this convention, making it one of the most popular international environmental agreements. The convention lists more than 400 World Heritage Sites as places judged to be of outstanding and universal significance, and the "common heritage of humankind." However, designation as a World Heritage Site does not ensure protection, and many sites are compromised — most by human activities, some by natural disasters.

Sources

UNESCO World Heritage Centre. *World Heritage List.* UNESCO: New York, 1994; World Conservation Monitoring Centre. *Global Biodiversity.* New York: Chapman and Hall, 1993; World Conservation Monitoring Centre/IUCN. *Protected Areas of the World.* Gland, Switzerland: IUCN, 1992.

34 TURNING GREEN

Individuals, community grassroots associations, and organized environmental groups are almost always ahead of their governments in identifying the causes of environmental degradation and in demanding solutions. But environmental concern has also now become part of the mainstream of social, political and economic current affairs. Environmental groups have presented environmental issues and the politics of environmental protection to a wide and increasingly active public. As people become better informed, national governments are being held directly accountable. "Green consciousness" can be a powerful force: environmental concerns, for example, were prominent in catalyzing the political unrest that eventually led to the breakup of the USSR.

In most of the industrialized world, environmental clean-up has become a profitable business. Ironically, some of the same companies that made money by polluting the world are now making more in their attempts to clean it up.

Sources:
The Economist. 20 November 1993 and 5 March 1994; Gallup International Institute. *Health of the Planet.* Princeton, NJ: Gallup, 1993; McCormick, John. *British Politics and the Environment.* London: Earthscan, 1991; Greenpeace, Friends of the Earth, World Wide Fund for Nature, personal communications.

35 STATE INTEREST

The International "Earth Summit" meetings held in Rio de Janiero, Brazil in 1992 made clear that inequities between the rich and poor are at the root of many environmental threats. This is true not only between rich and poor people, as Map 1 shows, but also between rich and poor states. Global inequality in wealth and power between states hampers the capacity of poor countries to sustain, let alone improve, the quality of life for their citizens. In the 1990s, poor states are facing a massive international debt whilst, at the same time, foreign aid is harder to come by, trading terms are deteriorating, and protectionism is growing in developed market economies.

The foreign debt accumulated by poor countries has become a major environmental problem. Most of the world's poorest countries are now exploiting their natural resources at escalating and unsustainable rates in order to earn the export income they desperately need in order to meet debt repayments and development pressures. As the World Commission on the Environment and Development noted in the late 1980s, "For many poor states, economic expansion can only be achieved at the price of ecological stress."

The financing for environmental initiatives in poor countries must come in large measure from rich countries. Traditionally poor countries have been helped by foreign aid, but throughout the 1980s many rich countries reduced their aid donations. Moreover, foreign aid often bears little relation to need: middle-income countries receive more than twice as much aid per person as low-income countries. A new initiative for providing environmental assistance to the poor world is the "debt-for-nature" swap. The first debt-for-nature swap was established in1987 to restructure part of Bolivia's foreign debt. Since then, debt-for-nature swaps have become an increasingly common debt restructuring device with 31 further swaps concluded in15 countries.

The Global Environmental Facility (GEF) was established on a trial basis in 1991 to provide funds to poor countries to undertake projects which address environmental problems with global impacts; in 1994, commitments for continuing and expanding the GEF were affirmed, and funding over the next few years should total nearly $2 billion.

Sources:
Global Environmental Facility (GEF), Washington, D.C. donor list; United Nations Environment Programme UNEP). *Our Planet.* 5 (5) 1993; U.S. Department of the Treasury; World Bank. *World Debt Tables 1993-94.* Washington, D.C.: World Bank, 1994; World Bank. *World Development Report 1993.* New York: Oxford University Press, 1993; World Commission on Environment and Development. *Our Common Future.* New York: Oxford University Press, 1987.

INDEX